DISCOVERY, INVENTION, RESEARCH

Fritz Zwicky

DISCOVERY, INVENTION, RESEARCH

Through the Morphological Approach

ILLUSTRATED WITH DRAWINGS AND DIAGRAMS

The Macmillan Company

CONTENTS

DISCOVERY, INVENTION, RESEARCH

INTRODUCTION

Since time immemorial men have worked toward making life easier. They have always searched for better ways to secure for themselves food, shelter, clothing, health, recreation, and pleasure. Many have also striven to excel in physical and spiritual accomplishments, while others have created works of art. And most of them have tried to understand the world, each after his fashion, thus endowing their lives with a deeper meaning.

On the way to these desired goals man has realized immense achievements throughout the millennia. His practical and theoretical knowledge, as well as his various capabilities, have multiplied and been enriched at an accelerated rate. The accumulated treasure of experience and technical knowledge available to us today is enormous. Thinkers of all ages have drawn their conclusions from these experiences and have formulated principles of wisdom, which, if they had been heeded, would have enabled individuals and humanity as a whole to reach all desired goals fully and easily. The fact that, contrary to this expectation the principles of wisdom were not heeded, and that we have not been able to prevent the ever recurring waste and degradation of human lives and valuable and irreplaceable spiritual and material treasures, must be due to some very particular causes. To recognize the nature of these causes and institute remedies for their elimination has been the endeavour of some of the best minds of all times. But no significant improvements in the events of the world have as yet been achieved. This can only mean that the various causes that the great thinkers visualized as being responsible for humanity's disregard of the generally agreed upon principles of wisdom cannot be the true and decisive ones. This is the more astounding since religious leaders, great philosophers, statesmen, and scientists have worked with the utmost dedication toward the realization of the principles and directives, which they had discovered and convincingly formulated.

The surprising, and at first unbelievable, conclusion that we are forced to draw from the described failures is this: In spite of all thought, all research, and all constructive work and sacrifice, some essential aspects must have been overlooked or disregarded. In his endeavour to develop sure means for the discovery of the causes that are at the root of the basic ills of the world, the author conceived of the morphological approach. The present book deals in a comprehensive way with this type of procedure and this type of philosophy. It attempts to illustrate the power of morphological thinking and planning as applied to a number of practical problems, and it describes some of the more impressive and startling results already achieved. The book closes with a preview and discussion of future developments.

Nuclear physics, after the dropping of the atom bombs on Hiroshima and Nagasaki, confronted us with the choice: *One World or None.* This means that we either construct our world in unison, or it will sooner or later be doomed. Whether this is correct or not, may I, in any case, express my very personal opinion that our efforts to achieve *One World* are most likely to succeed if we avail ourselves of the morphological approach, making the utmost use of the morphological methods of analysis and construction. I am inclined to think that only experienced morphologists will be capable of building a sound and stable organic world that embraces all peoples and individuals. We must strive toward the realization of what I visualize as the *Morphological Age* unless we are willing to see the world end in chaos and disintegration. The purpose of this book is to demonstrate that the morphological approach is our best hope of salvation.

It should be mentioned here that our first great goal is the evolution and completion of a mental *World Image*—which will allow us to visualize and comprehend all of the essential interrelations among physical objects, phenomena, concepts and ideas, as well as to evaluate the human capabilities needed for all future constructive activities. The fact that *total research* of this type, which is indispensable for the realization of a unified world, has not been carried out before is probably due to the fact that few men think in universal terms and vast perspectives. Most of them cling to concrete details and proceed only with difficulty from the special to the general, while the reverse course, starting from powerful general principles, appears to them hardly possible at all without previous instruction and training. They thus practice what might be called coastal navigation along clearly discernible shore lines of well-established knowledge and they do not dare to venture on the high seas of thought and action where the horizons are unlimited. Those few who start from limited vantage points, trying to achieve universal perspectives, seldom succeed. In fact, they most often end up in situations and predicaments worse than those from which they started unless they let themselves be guided by some reliable principles, such as that of the *Morphological Field Coverage*, which we shall discuss later. Religious leaders, philosophers, and scientists have all attempted since antiquity to construct a universal and true world image. Unfortunately, most of these creations were so unrealistic that they did not endure. A few religions and philosophies, of course, did correctly appraise some of the material and spiritual aspects of the world. Since, however, they at the same time either disregarded or suppressed other important aspects, they all eventually fell prey to internal contradictions, destructive assaults, and conflicts. Each in turn became less and less effective and none among them succeeded in stabilizing the world.

Morphological analysis and morphological planning and execution of large-scale projects have been conceived for the express purpose of properly appraising *all* of the facts (or, scientifically speaking, the boundary conditions) needed for the unbiased deduction of the possible solutions to any given problem. Only after all of these solutions have been thoroughly evaluated do we select that one among them that best satisfies our requirements.

I repeat, absolute detachment from all prejudice and a thorough acquaintance with all the essential elements, or pegs of knowledge, are the indispensable prerequisites for the successful use of the morphological approach. These "pegs of knowledge" refer to the characteristics of the objects of the material world as well as the nature of the physico-chemical phenomena that govern their interactions. In addition, we need a deep understanding of the psychological and spiritual traits of individuals and peoples, paying particular attention to the aberrations of the human mind. Morphological research and morphologically planned execution of significant projects can be appreciated and successfully achieved only by truly free men. In fact, we here visualize the emergence of an important new profession—namely that of the morphologist. The realization of the *One and Unified World* to which we have already alluded depends on how many free men and women will dedicate themselves to this new profession, educate and train themselves correspondingly, and spare no effort to work for those great goals that they and their spiritual kin have found worth striving for.

Right at the outset attention must be called to the important fact that the great goals of the morphologist are twofold. While the existence of man and his world must be safeguarded, his physical and spiritual potentialities must also be properly developed. To start with, then, we must take care to preserve both our individual existence and that of humanity as a whole. Only after we succeed in this can we hope to work effectively on the build-up of all human potentialities. The difficulty of safeguarding our existence and not allowing the gains made in the past to be lost should not be underestimated. Indeed, we have in our time had drastic evidence of the misdeeds and atrocities of big and small dictators, of parasites and exploiters of all kinds whose actions have repeatedly brought the whole world to the brink of disaster. There is no automatic guarantee that we shall be spared similar threats in the future. On the contrary, we must at all times be prepared for the emergence of monomaniacs of various calibers who will reach for that empty throne, one of which, according to Mussolini, exists in every country. In addition, our existence is being continually and increasingly endangered by the highly undesirable by-products that almost unavoidably accompany all modern technological progress. The disastrous influence and effects of various malignant features of our civilization must be strictly controlled and ultimately completely eliminated or neutralized if we are to survive. I refer in this connection to the noxious influences of insecticides and other chemicals on various agricultural products; the degradation of foods through the processes of artificial conservation; the pollution of the atmosphere by the exhausts from automobiles and industrial plants; the contamination of the water supplies; the radioactive poisoning of earth, water, and air as a result of civilian and military applications of nuclear energy; the rapidly increasing use of drugs of all descriptions whose temporary and long term effects on man and his descendants are as yet unknown; as well as many other health-endangering agents. Furthermore, the number of more or less unbalanced minds appears to be increasing alarmingly, a fact for which psychiatrists put much of the blame on the damaging aspects of the industrial age and the growing mechanization and automation of life. In any event, we cannot immediately commit all our strength to a further development of the promising potentialities inherent in man and society, but must first prevent the degeneration or the complete destruction of the values we already possess. Many of the present ills of the world could have been prevented had science and technology been properly employed. The fact that scientists and engineers have instead followed their own selfish goals is one of the great tragedies of our age. Fortunately, a change in attitude is on the horizon. Some of the most farsighted professionals are beginning to realize that schools in general, and universities in particular, must adopt programs foɪ teaching science and engineering more effectively. Accordingly, students can be brought to recognize the necessity of making their acquired skills available for the achievement of broad human goals. Mankind can no longer tolerate the exploitation of their skills solely for the sake of personal ambition. Among the many educators who occupy important and influential positions and who are actively promoting the education of scientists, physicians, and engineers to a universal sociological outlook I mention only the present president of Princeton University, Robert F. Goheen, who admonishes the entering students as follows:

> Late though the hour is, if any of you has come to Princeton hoping only to accumulate knowledge, I would advise you to begin immediate negotiations with some other sort of institution where you can attach yourself to a pipeline of inanimate learning and become full, like a storage tank, sealed by a diploma, and otherwise useless.

It is gratifying to notice that educators who agree with President Goheen's view are becoming more numerous.

It is slowly being recognized that the drift of many scientific and technical groups into ever greater isolation from the general public must be arrested and reversed. The unfortunate tendency toward a divided society was recently highlighted by a remark of one of my oldest friends at the California Institute of Technology who said to me: "Fritz, when we came to the Institute in 1925 we found very few students who had an interest in general human problems. Today we have none of these at all, and what's more, we do not even have any students who are really interested in science. They study it only to achieve some very selfish ends."

In any event, it would appear to be high time that we attempt to enlighten men and women of all ages, inspire them, and show them how to cooperate with the scientists and the engineers in building a sound world. Morphological research considers this program one of its most urgent goals. Some of the new ideas and procedures—which have been conceived by morphologists and already put into practice for training in different professions and for a more satisfactory use of available leisure time—will be discussed in later chapters. Along the suggested lines of thinking it appeared particularly important to begin with a basic reorientation of adults to help guide them through successive stages of positive collaboration between scientists and the general public, in order to bridge the unfortunate gap that now exists. Indeed, every normal adult has the right and the duty to express his opinion on all vital issues and decisions of his people. Many of these decisions can be made sensibly only on the basis of scientific knowledge, the basic character of which must thus be understood by all those who vote. Every ordinary citizen is also a taxpayer. He is therefore entitled to be informed about the use of public funds, and these often go into technical projects the nature of which he must understand. Furthermore, children who want to become scientists, physicians, or engineers may need the guidance and advice of their parents, which can be given only if they themselves keep in touch with the progress in science and technology. Finally, attention must be called to the little-recognized fact that many of our specifically technical problems cannot be solved easily if we have to forego the collaboration of thousands, and in some cases actually millions, of knowledgeable laymen and trained amateurs.

Among the many beginnings made to establish closer contacts between the various sciences and the general public, I mention the so-called *Seminar in the Newspaper*, which was organized by several scientists in collaboration with the Swiss Association for the Education of Adults. During the winter of 1962–63, seventeen articles on "The World as Seen by the Scientists: Preservation and Development of the Potentialities of Man through Discovery, Invention, Research" appeared in eight large daily newspapers in Switzerland. The subjects treated in these articles were subsequently discussed in more detail in evening courses conducted by the Association. Eight of my articles, which were printed in the *Seminar in the Newspaper*, have been incorporated, in part, in the present book. The first two of these articles, which constitute the first chapter, deal with the necessity already mentioned for all responsible adults to be kept continually informed about all important advances in science and technology, and also to be encouraged to cooperate actively with men of research.

The basic elements of the *Morphological World Image* are sketched and discussed in the second chapter. Later chapters describe the various methods most characteristic for the morphological approach and those that make possible the exhaustive analysis of problems in all fields of human endeavor, as well as the deduction, evaluation, and practical realization of entire complexes of possible solutions to these problems. In short, we shall attempt to show how the morphological approach inspires the imagination to ever new visions and advances, and how almost automatically the surest ways to discovery, invention, and new avenues of research reveal themselves.

The book closes with a presentation of the general goals of morphological research as they are being pursued actively by a professional nonprofit society founded specifically for this purpose. The *Society for Morphological Research* (with international membership and headquarters in Pasadena) is not only interested in the solution of a multitude of practical problems, but also plans to publish a series of comprehensive scientific-technical monographs intended to acquaint the general public with all newly developed methods of research and the essential results achieved. It need not be specially emphasized that we hope in the course of time to subject all vital and basic problems of interest to individuals and the whole community alike to a morphological analysis in order to find the most reliable ways to successfully plan and construct a unified and organically sound world.

OVERCOMING THE ABERRATIONS OF THE HUMAN MIND

I wish to stress in this introduction that the correct World Image probably would have been recognized long ago were it not for aberrations of the human mind, inertia of thought and action, and the paralyzing influence of sterile dogmas. The study of history shows that real progress is due, in the first place, to the elimination, step by step, of dogmas and taboos, of fear, and of human aberrations of all kinds. The discovery within the World Image of the ever new aspects that better represent the real facts of life, as well as the invention of new work-saving devices and methods and the exploration and application of the results of research and discovery, are often achieved with amazing ease if certain entrenched dogmas have first been recognized as such and eliminated. In this connection attention should be called to the remarkable, but nevertheless understandable, fact that the fight against calcified beliefs and their elimination are almost invariably to be credited to "lone wolves," who were usually soundly denounced during their lifetime and often persecuted by their contemporaries. As far as I know, very few among the larger organizations have ever succeeded in rendering services of similar inestimable value to mankind.

Notwithstanding the profound distrust with which they view any and all kinds of hierarchy, morphologists believe in the ultimate necessity of planned collaboration. Provided only that it is *free men and women* who work together, they will be able to recognize life-stifling dogmas and deal with them more effectively than can single individuals. We are, of course, impressed by Friedrich Schiller's William Tell, who proclaims, "The strong is the mightiest alone." And we are inclined to follow his advice in the present state of the world, which is ruled by so many hierarchies of selfish, neuroses-riddled, or senile men. Nevertheless, we are determined to show William Tell wrong for the future, inasmuch as we are convinced that a sound world can be built only if truly independent men will combine their knowledge and strength and collaborate in a new way, as visualized by the morphological approach.

The elimination of dogmas does not, of course, always and immediately lead to true progress. Regress may also result if an old, deadly doctrine is replaced by a new and still more dangerous one.

I emphasize again, the fight against human aberrations represents the most urgent task for the morphologist. As Friedrich Nietzsche said, "Man is something that must be overcome," meaning that the "human-all-too-human" within us must be clearly recognized and eliminated if we are to reach our goal as envisioned in the Bible: "Know the truth and the truth shall set you free."

In view of the dire state of the world one might expect that scientists and philosophers would make it their main task to complete a comprehensive *World Image*, which not only incorporates all of the available technical knowledge, but is free of internal conflicts and is humanly meaningful in the sense that those who thoroughly comprehend all its features will clearly recognize in it the unique guidelines for their own future actions. Some scientists are actually at work constructing the true World Image, but they are few and far between. In extension of my own work in physics, astronomy, jet-propulsion, and morphological research, I have often discussed with my students and colleagues ways and means of pooling our knowledge and collaborating with nonscientists in work on projects of general human interest. As an example I mention a series of seminars arranged in the summer of 1960 by the chief scientist of the United States Air Force, Dr. Knox Millsaps, at Cloudcroft, near Alamogordo, New Mexico. In the course of these seminars, I spoke about the dangerous effects of human aberrations on the state of the world. Dr. Wayne Gruner, program director for physics at the National Science Foundation in Washington, D.C., attended these seminars and reviewed some of my remarks in August 1962 in the following excellent manner:

ABERRATIONS DISPELLED

All are aware that, from the standpoint of society, scientific research has a dual motivation—pragmatic and idealistic. The former is obvious; the latter generally turns out to be very difficult to discuss incisively. Part of the difficulty, however, may be removed by Fritz Zwicky's observation that: "The great social contribution of science has been that of *dispelling aberrations of the human mind."*

To those who imagine that "dispelling aberrations of the mind" is the same as alleviating ignorance, we may point out that aberration goes beyond ignorance. I take Zwicky's remark to be a profound one containing the idea that ignorance per se is much less dangerous than the myths, superstitions, slogans, and like synthetic constructs with which mankind frantically stuffs the void of mere ignorance presumably to escape acknowledging the existence of any void.

The irrational urge to compound ignorance with superstition must be the reading of "aberrations of the human mind" in Zwicky's context. Does not history bear him out?

Perhaps by taking Zwicky seriously we can develop some criteria as to the level and the kind of scientific research which is required to meet this therapeutic need of society. We will advocate research addressed to those areas of ignorance which one can recognize as the immediate occasion of virulent aberration. One may amuse oneself in private with the enumeration of these. In addition, some level of research and scientific teaching is desirable to instill appreciation of the method and of its past and present role in dispelling aberrations.

Nothing is here said about the pure aesthetic satisfaction which is conveyed by science, and which I regard as the other important component of its idealistic motivation.

I mention here only a few of the numerous aberrations of the human mind, dogmas, and superstitions of which science has disposed, thus enabling man to appraise life more realistically. For instance, people once believed that the earth was flat and that the sea west of Gibraltar was populated by dreadful monsters and was therefore too dangerous to be traversed. As a consequence the ancients dared to navigate only along the well-known coasts of the Mediterranean. As a matter of fact, the Greek astronomers already knew the earth to be a sphere, and Erathostenes (276–194 B.C.) had determined its circumference with remarkable accuracy. In spite of this, one and a half millennia passed before Columbus dared to sail the wide open seas and discover America.

Almost equally persistent was the dogma that the earth is the center of the universe. This fixed idea retarded the discovery that planetary orbits around the sun are simple ellipses and recognition of the nature of the basic laws of kinematics, dynamics, and gravitation as they were later formulated by Kepler, Galileo, and Newton. And what was more unfortunate yet, for doubting the dogmas of Aristotle during the dark ages, a still unknown number of so-called heretics faced merciless persecution; many of whom lost their lives.

Even in arithmetic there appeared, and still persist today, all sorts of superstitious notions and dogmas that impede new discoveries and insights. The old Greeks, for instance, were perfectionists in the sense that they thought everything to be related to whole numbers. They did not know of the existence of irrational numbers (the square root of 2 is such a number), or in any case they did not dare to doubt the exclusive sovereignty of the whole number and they consequently got stalled in their mathematical researches.

The confusion and the disasters that have been caused by the activities of astrologers, occultists, fortune-tellers, and swindlers juggling mysterious numbers and devices and predicting future events from phony theories about the effects of the stars and planets on the life of man would fill volumes. I refer the reader to the book *l'Astrologie* by Professor P. Couderc (Presses Universitaires de France, Paris, 1951).

In this connection it would be interesting to find out to what extent the widespread superstition about the number 13 and black "Friday the 13th" interferes with present day international traffic and other aspects of life. And what is the actual origin of this fear of the number 13?

Furthermore, what is one to think of a former high-ranking member of the United States government who, in obvious terror, removes my hat from the bed in my hotel room in Washington, D.C., as if this, for every sane person, harmless contact between two geometric objects could presently cause the death of one of us. (Morphologists will nevertheless ponder the possibility that a person subject to such superstitions might actually get killed in some accident because of absentmindedness while worrying about the hat on the bed and consequently getting killed in traffic or falling down some stairs.)

To us astronomers it is a sad fact that more and more newspapers and journals, which pretend to enlighten the public about scientific progress, publish trashy columns with astrological prophecies. Considering the publishers it can be understood, but it must be soundly condemned that the morbid fantasies of a superstitious public are abetted in this manner. Since, however, part of the blame must go to us astronomers and to our colleagues in medicine, psychology, and other learned fields, I briefly invoke here the morphological method of *Negation and Construction* for some guiding suggestions. This method, based on one of the most fundamental principles of thought and procedure, will be discussed later on in greater detail.

We astronomers know that birth at some date when the sun passes through this or that constellation of the Zodiac in no way predetermines the course of life because of any possible influence of said constellation of stars (which in any case is only an apparent one, a projection on the celestial sphere of stars that are not neighbors at all but are located at widely different distances in space). Most astronomers, therefore, will let the issue rest with the flat statement that all astrology is complete nonsense. The morphologist, however, prefers to follow up any negation with constructive action, which alone can ultimately succeed in enlightening a gullible public about the baselessness of astrology and in many cases the crooked intentions of those who practice it. To be constructive we must make a much greater effort to inform the general public about our investigations of the real happenings in cosmic space. Yet we must not neglect to find out what specific natural phenomena might actually exist that occasionally but *coincidentally* bear out some prediction made by an astrologer. This suggests the following ideas.

First, as already stated, we must inform the public about the results of our research, not via the magazines that dramatize, editorialize, and garble the material in their usual inept way, but directly. Second, a group of physicians, biologists, meteorologists, geographers, and other competent specialists should investigate how far birth in various seasons and climactic conditions, at different altitudes and in different countries, and choice of foods and feeding habits influence the physical and mental development of children. It is certainly not the arrangement or the character of stars in the constellation of Virgo, or any other signs of the Zodiac, that plays any role, but there could be a significance to the biologically and physically different conditions in various locations during the calendar months associated with the constellations of the Zodiac. One notices immediately that even this remote possibility cannot be of any comfort to astrologers, since June on the Northern Hemisphere climatically corresponds to December on the Southern. Last, the necessarily tolerant morphologist, who leaves no stone unturned, knows that in practice one cannot always proceed with the desired speed if disasters are to be avoided. He therefore will leave the misguided, weak, and superstitious with their aberrations and their chimeras, as long as they are happy and do not endanger the community. Nevertheless, we must not rest with our fight against all aberrations. How we may effectively proceed in this endeavor will be discussed in later sections and, in particular, in a book entitled *Everyone a Genius,* which the author hopes to issue in the near future.

A few examples may serve to illustrate how great advances in the sciences were achieved by breaking axioms and dogmas that had previously been thought to represent absolute truths. Then, some beliefs will be discussed that largely control and govern life today, and which must be overcome if we are to make any significant progress with the building of a sound world.

After the glorious achievement of Euclid (330–275 B.C.) and his successors in ancient Greece, no essential progress in geometry was made for two thousand years, except for the introduction of Analytical Geometry by René Descartes (1596–1650) and perhaps the descriptive and projective geometry developed by the great painters of the Renaissance and the French mathematicians of the eighteenth century. A tremendous innovation came first at the beginning of the nineteenth century, when N. I. Lobatchewski conceived of a new type of geometry that negates the validity of Euclid's fifth axiom and proceeds without making any use of it. This so-called axiom of the parallels states that through a point, A, outside of a straight line, s, there exists only one straight line, s, which lies in the plane defined by A and s, which does not intersect s and is therefore parallel to it. Lobatchewski's *Hyperbolic Geometry*, which he developed, disregarding the axiom of the parallels, led to the study during the nineteenth century of a great number of non-Euclidean spaces that later enabled Einstein to formulate his *Theory of Relativity*. Along the same lines of thought further great advances were made after Einstein broke the belief in an *absolute time* and *a unique absolute real space*, which Immanuel Kant, and all scientists and philosophers after him, had thought to be the only possible ones.

Finally, our understanding of the world of atoms was extraordinarily deepened after the absolute validity of the *causality axiom*, once one of the most important bulwarks of classical physics, was negated. As is well known, the resulting generalization of the concept of causality enabled Werner Heisenberg (1901–   ) and Erwin Schrödinger (1887–1961) to formulate the theory of quantum mechanics, which so successfully represents entire complexes of microscopic phenomena not formerly understood in classical physics.

(I should mention here that I agree with Einstein in his belief that quantum mechanics does not really represent the final truth, and that the law of causality in some future more universal theory will again be accorded a more important role. Readers who are interested in following this conjecture may consult my book *Morphological Astronomy*, Springer Verlag, Berlin, 1957.)

Scientists have thus learned to doubt and to negate what claim to be absolute truths, to disregard axioms and dogmas, and to evolve and perfect ever more universal concepts and theories in order to arrive at a growing understanding of the world around us. Unfortunately, with these advances also came some undesirable side effects: A great number of scientists as well as laymen fell prey to the overbearing and presumptuous belief that scientific truth is absolute and science omniscient. This fallacious notion caused, or is associated with, the emergence of those groups and organizations of men of research and scholars who successfully work on problems of limited scope, but who unduly promote each other to the exclusion of free and lone investigators. They pass stipends, honors, prizes, and other kudos among themselves and in this manner misguide oncoming youth through their glorification of false values, at the same time neglecting their human responsibilities, thus lowering their ethical standards in a most regrettable way.

Largely because of the shortsightedness and the selfishness of these purportedly enlightened individuals and their glorification of limited and doubtful values, we have failed so far to overcome the aberrations of the minds of Fascists, Communists, and ruthless capitalists, as well as the dogmas, prejudices, and superstitions of the various religions and sects. As a result, we have not yet been able to realize a free, stable, and harmonious human community.

Our greatest and most unrelenting efforts will have to be devoted to breaking the long entrenched and vicious beliefs in the supremacy of certain selected types of individuals, races, and peoples. These beliefs probably represent the greatest obstacles on our way to an emotionally stabilized human society. Like many others, I have long pondered the difficult problem of how to expose and overcome the prejudices involved and I hope to present some constructive proposals in my aforementioned book, *Everyone a Genius*.

1

Safeguarding the Existence of Man and of His Potentialities through Discovery, Invention, and Research

A well-known physicist complained recently that the atom was once our friend but has now become our deadly enemy. He meant that atomic (nuclear) energy, which had been both harnessed and released by the scientists, had subsequently been appropriated by irresponsible men in power. As a result, mankind is in danger of being annihilated in a third world war or by decimation and slow death because of the excessive accumulation of radioactive agents in the atmosphere, water, and food supplies. For the responsible and conscientious scientist the most important problem, therefore, is spelled out by the alternative *One World or None* as I have already emphasized in the Introduction. This means that if men do not succeed in living with one another in harmony and justice in order to transform the present confused and divided world into an orderly and organic whole, there exists a real danger that the human community is approaching its twelfth hour.

How this all happened we shall try to discuss later. In addition, it will be most important to show what not only every scientist and professional but all men can do to avoid the conflicts leading to genocide, and how they can help, instead, to safeguard the existence and the development of the potentialities of man.

17

The catastrophic dilemma confronting us today did not arise from one day to the next as the lamenting physicist, mentioned above, might make us believe. Our difficulties, rather, have their origin in the way discovery, invention, and research have been conducted in the past and how the results achieved have been applied both constructively and destructively in all fields of human endeavor. If we are correct in this view it follows that discovery, invention, and research in the future must be handled in a new way and by men of deeper insight than was exhibited by the professionals of the past.

I wish to make it clear that I have no intention of acting as a prophet or a preacher of morals. The reader, however, should realize that for a man of research, who loves life and the world, there is no more unpardonable irresponsibility than to remain inactive while this life is being destroyed, or worse yet, to accelerate its doom directly or indirectly through selfish behavior and stupid mechination. How scientists must proceed to aid in the development of all of the valuable potentialities of man becomes evident immediately from a study of the history and characters of discovery, invention, research, and technology. This study not only furnishes the means with which to safeguard our existence but reveals their effectiveness by expanding and enriching our lives in an unexpected measure.

It must be emphasized from the start that the creation of a free world, which is to be organized and managed by judicious leaders, depends upon the following conditions, which must be firmly established through the collaboration of the general public with the specialists of all fields.

To start, it is imperative that men of research in all countries get together in order to promote those scientific and technological problems that relate to the most urgent needs of the human community.

Furthermore, all professionals must prevent the abuse and misuse of the results of their work by stupid, selfish, or power-hungry individuals and chauvinistic peoples.

And finally, the scientists must not only inform all of their co-citizens of the implications of their work and inspire them to make good use of the knowledge acquired when decisions on civic issue are at stake, but they must also teach them how to collaborate directly and indirectly in professional investigations and research. This latter possibility has not been clearly recognized and made use of in the past, a neglect that has contributed much to the alarming increase in the number of conflicts and catastrophes in the world. For this reason the continuation of education for adults of all age groups is indispensable, and we must seriously try to demonstrate that the man in the street need no longer remain a mere onlooker, but very well may, and actually must, become an active collaborator in research.

DISCOVERY, INVENTION, AND RESEARCH IN THE PAST

The morphological evaluation of the discoveries, inventions, and research during the past several thousand years shows that they were preponderantly by lone investigators. Their accomplishments resulted in a tremendous accumulation of facts and insights relating to the happenings in the world. But they also gave rise to the erroneous idea that genius is something extraordinary and not given to every man and woman. This historical study further reveals that the applications of discoveries, inventions, and the results of research were often jeopardized, and even tragically misused, inasmuch as dubious and even criminal individuals exploited the new knowledge thereby gained for their own selfish purposes and to the detriment of mankind.

By way of illustration it may be pointed out that the *discovery* of America led to the annihilation of many of the indigenous races and of some of their magnificent cultures. The exploration and exploitation of conquered lands was furthermore institutionalized in a most unfortunate type of colonialism, the consequences of which we must now bear.

The *invention* of language is one of the earliest and most re-markable accomplishments of the human mind. But what devastating effects have been caused in our age through the criminal misuses of language for purposes of propaganda by so many power-hungry and malicious individuals, culminating in men such as Stalin and Hitler. The fact that the discoveries of dynamite, radio transmission, the airplane, and rockets gave war its present-day character is, of course, common knowledge. Harnessing of atomic energy bodes worse for the future.

The misuse of the fruits of scientific *research* that has been perpetrated by modern technology, commerce, and the various governments has caused pollution of the atmosphere and of water supplies and has so degraded and partly poisoned many of our foodstuffs that the resulting effects on the state of world health cannot as yet be evaluated. The crowning tragedy occurred when the results of nuclear physics research were not only incorporated into devices *to be held ready for defense* against any dangerous attacks on free peoples, but were then actually and tragically used by them *first* for offensive warfare. This has caused an almost in-eradicable universal mistrust, which is forcing every nation to develop its own atomic weapons. Furthermore, even without a war in our age of uneasy peace, the earth's atmosphere may become hopelessly polluted by the radioactive fallout that will result from any undisciplined experimentation, and which, in the end, may lead to genocide.

The reader will be able to think easily of other examples illustrating how we literally blundered into the ages of modern science and technology, international commerce and traffic, and particularly into the atomic age. The reader will no doubt agree with me, also, that after this sad record we cannot afford to let humanity start its march into outer space (the solar system and beyond) and the march into inner space (the interior of the earth and of the oceans) in an equally senseless manner if we wish to endure.

COLLABORATION OF THE MEN OF RESEARCH WITH THE COMMUNITY: COLLECTIVE ENDEAVOUR IN ADDITION TO INDIVIDUAL EFFORT

If we are to progress with our plans for a sound society, we obviously must strive to make rational use of all the work done by discoverers, inventors, and scientists, and we must prevent the misuse of their achievements. To establish useful guidelines for procedure, it is helpful to study the accomplishments of some of the great men of the past, who dedicated their efforts toward the development of all the valuable potentialities inherent in man. Such names as Paracelsus, Johann Heinrich Pestalozzi, Henri Dufour, Louis Pasteur, and Fridtjof Nansen remind us that, in contrast to the innumerable self-centered men of research whose names are better forgotten, there were those shining knights who did their utmost to use the results of their research for the enrichment of the life of the community. In recognition of such efforts the simple people of Einsiedeln, Switzerland, on a simple block of granite inscribed their thoughts about their not-so-simple co-citizen Paracelsus:

> To the Memory of The Physician, Scientist,
> and Philosopher Theophrastus Paracelsus,
> Rejuvinator of Medicine, Father of Chemotherapy,
> Successful Biologist and Surgeon.
> Saviour of those of Clouded Mind,
> Promoter of Medical Ethics,
> Independent Thinker and Devout Christian,
> Friend of the Poor,
> Born in the fall of 1493 Near the
> Devil's Bridge at the Foot of the Etzel,
> Lived a Faustian Life, and
> Died on September 24, 1541 at Salzburg,
> Longing for his Native Country.

To Pestalozzi (1746–1827) we owe the idea, which I consider the most important for the future of man, that all must be given the opportunity to learn, to train themselves, and to be guided so as to recognize each his own unique genius. Any successful co-operation of the men of research among themselves and with all men is quite unthinkable without Pestalozzi's philosophy and pedagogy. Before him, the knowledge accumulated through thousands of years of discovery, invention, and research was accessible only to a privileged few. Misuse of this knowledge was common and caused innumerable conflicts and catastrophes, preventing the construction of a harmonious world.*

Concerning the possibility of a constructive collaboration among the nations of the world, it should be mentioned that long before the Age of Rationalism some peoples, the old Swiss for instance, became enthusiastic about great thoughts such as freedom and the brotherhood of all men, and at times successfully fought for their realization. This inspires in us the confidence that we shall also succeed in bringing the scientists and the general public to work together for the preservation of mankind and the development of his hidden potentialities. Our confidence becomes a certainty when we think of the successes of men like Dufour, Pasteur, and Nansen.

---

* Among the many instances that could be cited testifying to Pestalozzi's deep human vision and making those who know of his work see each other as brothers and sisters, I mention the extraordinary case of the great Japanese philosopher and educator, Arata Osada, who asked that his ashes be buried next to Pestalozzi's grave in the cemetery of Birr, Switzerland. On his grave stone is written:

Here rest in fulfillment of his last personal
wish the ashes of the great admirer of Pestalozzi
Arata Osada
1887–1951
Professor of Pedagogy
at the University of Hiroshima
Honorary Doctor
of the University of Zurich
in recognition of his untiring efforts
as founder of the great Pestalozzi movement
in Japan
and as translator and editor of Pestalozzi's
works in the Japanese language
and friend and admirer
of the Swiss democracy.

Henri Dufour (1787–1875), engineer, inventor, topographer, originator of the Dufour map of Switzerland—which represented the greatest breakthrough in map-making in many centuries—and great military leader succeeded in terminating the Swiss Civil War of 1847 without any bloodshed through an unmatched strategic positioning of his armies. By the same superior stratagems he made an ascending and already overbearing Bismarck bow out of the so-called Neuchâtel incident and, in cooperation with Henri Dunant, crowned his great career with the founding of the International Red Cross and the formulation of the Geneva Convention.

Louis Pasteur (1822–95), discoverer of a cure for killing scourges of mankind, took unheard-of personal risks and with unrelenting persistence developed and applied the various agents for the prevention and cure of rabies, anthrax, and other infectious diseases.

And finally Fridtjof Nansen (1861–1930), who was in my estimation the greatest man of this century. This scientist and explorer made the first crossing of Greenland on foot, paved the way toward the North Pole, interfered forcefully to arbitrate the bitter conflict between Sweden and Norway, founded the international Nansen Bureau, and established the Nansen Passport for those hundreds of thousands who had become homeless after the first World War, and all of those refugees of later years who were without a country, and distributed the Nansen packages that saved the lives of millions of starving Russians in the early 1920s. Finally, this ingenious initiator and organizer arranged among the Balkan States and Turkey for the repatriation of many millions of Greeks, Turks, Bulgarians, Serbians, Macedonians, and others whose hundreds of years of living among other peoples had repeatedly been the cause of violent and bloody conflicts. And what was most astounding, through education and procurement of work for all who were transplanted, Nansen succeeded not only in insuring their livelihood, but also in helping to raise the economic and cultural standards of all the nations involved, which after centuries of strife became friends and in all probability would have stayed friends if Hitler, Stalin, and Mussolini had not upset the peaceful development Nansen had brought about.

Men like Dufour and Nansen must serve us as guiding spirits for the future. It is to be regretted that few books have been written about these men, and to my knowledge no adequate accounts at all in English. While these great men of universal stature are being forgotten by the much-touted "take-over generation" floods of articles and books are written about plain rabble. Like Nansen, all explorers, inventors, and men of research must wake up and realize that they were accorded special privileges by their fellow men and in return they have a duty to pursue the social implications of their work. Results achieved by specialists must be guided into constructive channels and not allowed to be misused.

Scientists must further come to realize that work on isolated projects is not sufficient. They must, in addition, pool their strength for co-operative efforts. The tasks humanity faces today, and especially the problems concerning large-scale planning for the future, are so complex that their solution requires well-considered and organized collaboration. The two examples of the International Astronomical Union and of the International Academy of Astronautics will be discussed later on in order to show that effective collaboration among the scientists of all peoples is really possible.

One further requirement has already been stressed. All men must constantly be kept informed about the essential aspects of new discoveries, invention, and research. Laymen, as well as the pure and applied scientists themselves, must be made to realize that there is a task for us, that everybody may not only passively look on, but can also actively participate in the achievement of scientific and technological advances. How this is possible can be explained in two simple examples, namely the measures that must be taken in order to eliminate the smog over Los Angeles and other cities, and the many problems related to national defense. Additional circumstances requiring the combined attention of both the professional specialists and the general public will be pointed out as we go along.

Beyond safeguarding our existence by means of the measures just described, life can be enriched immeasurably if people generally begin to realize that the concept of the *dignity of man* really implies that, literally speaking, *everyone is a genius,* that is that every individual is *unique, indispensable,* and *incomparable.* We hold that every man, without exception, has his own and specifically creative character. It is therefore not sufficient that in the free countries much ado is made about the dignity of each individual, and that the various constitutions declare all citizens to be equal. True equality can be established only if the creative potentialities of every man, woman, and child are really recognized, and if everything is done to develop these priceless treasures.

Finally, in order to manage effectively all the difficulties both the individuals and the community face in modern life, new methods of thought and practical procedure must be invented and perfected, which are more universal and more effective than any of those available to us in the past.

The goals just stated have long been of deep concern to me. As a result, I have, during the past thirty years, conceived of the *Morphological Approach* and have implemented it through the development of a number of morphological methods of analysis and construction. I believe that this approach can make vital contributions toward the construction of a stable and organic society, mainly because of its peculiar ability to inspire deeper thinking, an ability and art that in our increasingly mercenary and ethically degenerating society has already become a rarity.

REORIENTATION OF THE MEN OF RESEARCH

To illustrate the necessary guidelines for planning the future, attention must be called to several facts and proposals. We note first that collective actions among discoverers, inventors, and men of research are already in the making. Two specific examples are the founding of the International Astronomical Union (IAU) almost fifty years ago and the International Academy of Astronautics eight years ago. The former is made up of members who hail from eighty-five nations on both sides of the Iron Curtain. The IAU is particularly interested in organizing worldwide collaboration on those problems in astronomy that can be handled by individual investigators only with great difficulty or not at all. For example, the author of this book is chairman of the Committee for the Discovery and Research on Supernovae—the *Cosmic Atom Bombs*—whose observation furnishes us with important data on the size and evolution of the universe. The following observatories are participating in the discovery campaign for Supernovae: Palomar, Mount Wilson and Lick in the United States, Tonantzintla (Mexico), Cordoba (Argentina), Pretoria (South Africa), Stromlo (Australia), Crimea, Abastumani, and Byurakan (U.S.S.R), Konkoly (Hungary), Tautenburg (East Germany), Meudon (France), Asiago (Italy), and Zimmerwald (Switzerland). It should be emphasized that thousands of amateurs could materially help us in our sky surveys if they were properly instructed —an excellent example of possible collaboration of laymen and specialists in a highly intricate and sophisticated enterprise. Within the context of this book, however, it is of still greater significance that the IAU, as an absolutely neutral body, has already taken a resolute stand against all objectionable activities by nations whose governments allow or support types of experimentation that might lead to a general contamination, radioactive or otherwise, not only of earth, but also of the solar system and outer space. For instance the United States government some time ago admitted that nuclear bomb tests in greater heights had appreciably affected the distribution of electric charges in the radiation belts that surround the earth. Such artificially induced alterations can seriously affect observations made by astronomers and physicists of the cosmic rays and may also impede space navigation. The IAU clearly recognized the danger of our blundering thoughtlessly into the space age and strongly protested against all irresponsible experimentation.

The International Academy of Astronautics (IAA)—which represents a very compact body of experts from many nations, and in contradistinction to the IAU from all professional disciplines— has from its beginnings concerned itself with the formulation of a treaty for Outer Space (and partly for Inner Space) which is intended to be analogous to the Antarctic Treaty. The IAA considers one of its most urgent tasks to persuade all nations to sign such a treaty and to honor it. It will be remembered that the Antarctic Treaty is the first in the history of man that rationally plans and regulates the exploration and possible exploitation of a continent; Antarctica. In contradistinction to the age-old quarrels about the possession of this or that territory, the International Treaty of 1961 declares "It is in the interest of mankind that Antarctica be used exclusively and forever for peaceful purposes and that it not become the scene or the object of international conflicts." This agreement has so far been signed by eight nations, including the Soviet Union. Twelve nations have established about forty bases for research. The IAA proposes to all nations that the march into outer space be regulated and conducted in the same conciliatory spirit. In a later chapter (pp. 156–69) more will be said about this important subject.

COLLABORATION OF SCIENTISTS AND LAYMEN

Among the hundreds of cases in which it is of utmost importance that the public be kept informed about technical advances, in order that all involved may be able to co-operate in constructive actions, I mention the following two:

The first problem relates to the elimination of smog, which in many areas is so heavy that it constitutes a serious hazard to the health of the population and adversely affects the growth of plants. The term smog was formed by a fusion of the words smoke and fog and is used to describe an enrichment of the air with smoke and exhaust gases and evaporated chemicals of various origins. One of the cities most strongly affected is Los Angeles. Investigating chemists and physicists have found that about

10,000 tons of unburnt hydrocarbon fuels and organic solvents are released every day into the air over the County of Los Angeles. These agents, in combination with the nitrogen oxides exhausted from millions of automobiles, are photochemically acted upon by the light from the sun. As a result of this reaction various acids, ozone, and organic peroxides are generated, all of which are very irritating. To make things worse, the meteorological conditions in Southern California are such that because of a frequently existing temperature inversion with altitude, a layer one kilometer thick and perhaps two hundred kilometers in lateral extent lies motionless over the city and county becoming saturated with the aforementioned chemical compounds. This smog devastatingly irritates the eyes, dangerously lowers visibility at the different airports, hastens the disintegration of automobile tires and many other rubber products, badly soils the city, and so reduces the working potential of the population that enormous economic losses are sustained. After years of educational propaganda by chemists, physicists, and physicians, the politicians and the public finally agreed to some ordinances prohibiting installations that exhaust dangerous materials and outlawing the burning of all sorts of trash in backyard incinerators. The most important and most dangerous source of the smog over Los Angeles could not be eliminated, however, because neither the man in the street nor the politicians in their blindness and selfishness yet want to admit the simple fact that they themselves are responsible for the present contamination of the atmosphere, or that for the good of the community they must submit to some restrictions in the use of their cars. In this connection the value of close co-operation between scientists and laymen became strikingly evident inasmuch as our wives and nonacademic friends acted as survey teams, who on their many thousands of drives through Los Angeles collected statistical evidence showing that more than 95 per cent of the cars traveling on the city's freeways are occupied by the driver only. By the simple measure of taxing single drivers, half of the smog could be eliminated overnight. After I made this proposal (see the article "A Morphologist Ponders the Smog Problem,"

Engineering and Science Journal, Vol. 24, No. 2, pp. 22–26, California Institute of Technology, Nov. 1960), the resulting outcry of fury in letters to the local newspapers was something to behold, and one could only conclude that the number of neurotics is far greater than commonly assumed. In justice, it should, however, be emphasized that the press throughout the United States commented favorably on my various proposals. As a matter of fact it must be stressed that some of us professional scientists and engineers who have occupied ourselves with the problem know very well how the smog could be reduced materially within a few months, and how it could be entirely eliminated within a few years. We have here one of the few clear-cut cases where the scientist is far ahead in his investigations but has not succeeded in persuading his fellow citizens that they must speak up now decisively, for if they do not force the politicians to act, human lives will be lost in increasing numbers and tens of thousands of children will become permanently afflicted with all sorts of ailments and even be doomed to die of lung cancer and other illnesses.

As the second case for whose solution the collaboration of laymen, inventors, and men of research is indispensable, I mention the problem of national planning. This large-scale and complex task can be successfully dealt with only if rational procedures for the optimum utilization of the natural and social resources of a country are invented and perfected. *Ekistics* (the planning and construction of human settlements) and the streamlining of all traffic and communications are in the forefront, while by way of an absolutely necessary holding action, the military and the civilian defenses must also be made impregnable. Inasmuch as the universally oriented scientists, physicians, and engineers know in principle how these intricate problems must be effectively dealt with, the decisions for the actual realization of all vital projects rest largely with the ordinary citizen, who therefore must be kept informed at any cost of all the major developments in science and technology and must be inspired to collaborate constructively and unrelentingly with the experts.

THE MORPHOLOGICAL APPROACH

From what we have said, it follows that we can safeguard our existence and develop our potentialities effectively only if we succeed in developing and applying new methods of thought and procedure more powerful than any of those known in the past. I have already mentioned the morphological methods that I believe to be the most promising for the shaping of the life of the world in the future. Stating it succinctly, the *morphological approach* is equivalent with *totality research*. This approach, however, does not concern itself only with the *totality of all of the possible aspects and solutions of any given problem*. Beyond this it insists on exploring all the possibilities for practical application of the results achieved to insure the continued stabilization of human society and the enrichment and optimization of its activities. During the past twenty-five years morphological methods have been used with gratifying success for the invention of novel propellants and propulsive power plants; for problems in the textile industry; for large-scale surveys in observational astronomy and space research; for the development of powerful, analytical composite photography; and, most importantly, for new approaches to specialized and universal education and information for both children and adults. Because of its extraordinarily suggestive power, the morphological approach enables us to make discoveries and inventions systematically, not just one at a time, but whole classes of them simultaneously. And, most important, it inspires a very fruitful type of *profound thinking*, of which modern man is largely unaware or incapable. In what follows, we shall extensively occupy ourselves with the discussion of the various aspects of the morphological approach and describe some of the practical results achieved with it. I also claim that this approach leads us on the surest way to discovery of those human aberrations that are responsible for the ills of the world, and it will enable us to develop the means necessary for safe-guarding our existence, individually and collectively, as well as guide us on our way to co-operative action for the realization of a unified and stable world.

2

The Morphological World Image

In the introduction we suggested that the cause for mental aberrations of individuals and of peoples and the innumerable resulting conflicts and tragedies through the ages is to be looked for in the fact that men generally did not visualize nor properly appreciate and consult the correct world image. The neglect or the disregard of certain hard facts led to an unceasing sequence of false decisions and unfortunate actions, which, in unavoidable collision with reality, were doomed to end in confusion and disaster. If we wish to fare better than our predecessors, we must, before all, seek to know the correct *World Image* and we must constantly keep it before our eyes whenever we plan or make vital decisions and proceed to act. Otherwise we risk getting entrapped again and again by the ever-recurring age-old difficulties that interfered with all efforts to realize a sound world in the past.

But of what consists this true world image? Generally speaking, the world image of every individual is composed of the various aspects of an *inner world*, which is entirely his own, and of those of the *outer world*, which are common to all men. The outer world contains an immense multitude of material objects whose interactions are regulated by physico-chemical as well as biological

31

and psychological phenomena. Our inner world, however, knows of ideas, concepts, desires, imagery, emotions, motives and impulses for action, fear, and other states of the mind, both conscious and subconscious, which influence each other and, by way of the interactions between mind and body, exert a decisive influence on the happenings in the world and, therefore, can affect the inner worlds of others. Thus, the correct world image incorporates the true characteristics of the material objects and the natural phenomena that govern their interactions, as well as the spiritual contents of the minds of men. It is a true representation of all these aspects of life in the sense that it is free from internal discrepancies and can be clearly understood by every human being. He who is in possession of the correct world image will inherently be capable of predicting much of the future and will clearly see his way to new discoveries and inventions; he will thus be a potential leader in the search for the long-sought causes of human aberrations and the most effective means for their elimination.

In the present chapter an attempt will be made to sketch some of the important aspects of the true, or what might also be called the total, world image. To start with we shall introduce only experiences and insights known to every normal man. We repeat our previous warning, however, that neither the sum total of everyday knowledge available nor all the insights gained by the great thinkers throughout the ages have so far sufficed to bring about the realization of a stable and reasonable world.

The knowledge and insights gained about the outer world and the many inner worlds of men in the course of thousands of years are at least partly stored in the brains of the present generation. To a larger extent, they are recorded in the world's literature, and they are embodied in countless artifacts, buildings, and works of art. I propose to choose a few items from this monumental store of knowledge in order to show that next to the chosen and well-known ones some other pieces of information of great importance are suspected to exist but are as yet unknown. We must find these missing items to satisfactorily complete our world image, and this is precisely the first great task on which we morphologists have proposed to work. As will be shown later, the morphological method of infiltration and extrapolation into as yet unexplored domains lends itself particularly well to the stated purpose. This method starts from fixed points, or reliable *pegs* of presently available knowledge, and then proceeds to penetrate into *all* the surrounding and as yet unexplored territories.

The final goal of the method of relentless infiltration is what I have proposed to call a complete field coverage, that is an exhaustive exploration of all domains that lie between the initial pegs of knowledge, be they material or abstract in character. We speak therefore of the *Morphological Method of Field Coverage*, which has the great advantage of being universally applicable and easily understood. Trial by jury is a good example of how this method can be usefully applied in practice. Indeed, the justification for the choice of a court of this type is to be found in our conviction that every juror, if he is mentally normal and unprejudiced, will be able to understand and properly evaluate all the essential aspects of any case at hand, provided he makes a concerted effort to consider *all* of the circumstances that might be relevant. The fact that he can ultimately rely only on his common sense means that actually he is making use of the method of complete field coverage, knowingly, or, most likely, unknowingly. The extraordinary potential value of this method becomes particularly evident in those intricate criminal cases in which it would be a tragic mistake to search for the culprit in only a few more or less obvious directions. It is imperative to search in *all* directions; or, as the morphologist would say, the whole field of possibilities must be covered lest one risk, as unfortunately happens too often, finding the wrong man guilty and hanging him.

Our quest for the true world image, then, can be successful only if we explore *all* the avenues that might lead to the origin or cause of any phenomenon or happening we are trying to understand. (Jurors, for instance, must be clear about the origin and causes of a crime, and they must find the real culprit who committed it.) I repeat that in numerous analogous circumstances it is absolutely necessary that extended fields of possibilities be thoroughly surveyed.

How the method of morphological field coverage enables us to acquire total information about entire groups of objects and phenomena will be shown in the next chapter, where specific examples are discussed. To start, we restrict ourselves to the sketch of a few elements that form part of the morphological world image. In this connection we must emphasize that the great minds of all times have struggled with the construction of such a world image. The morphological approach naturally avails itself of and tries to make the best use of all the methods invented and developed by thinkers of the past as well as all of their specific achievements, if this appears appropriate and useful. Beyond that, however, the morphologist chooses his own peculiar ways, which are of the greatest universality and freedom from prejudice, and which he pursues with unrelenting vigor, never resting until the totality of the objects, circumstances, and phenomenological interrelations, within any given domain of the world image, one after the other appear clearly in focus and are understood. Beyond this, morphological research has led to the development of a number of powerful methods which, if used by unbiased investigators, almost automatically succeed, step by step, in completing the true world picture.

Attention must be called to the fact that the term *morphology* has long been used in many fields of science to designate research on structural interrelations—for instance in anatomy, geology, botany, and general biology. Goethe, in some limited way, thought in morphological terms, inasmuch as he tried to reduce the multitude of structural forms of plants and animals to a common denominator. I have proposed to generalize and systematize the concept of morphological research and include not only the study of the shapes of geometrical, geological, biological, and generally material structures, but also to study the more abstract structural interrelations among phenomena, actions, concepts, and ideas, whatever their character might be. One of the first, who like modern morphologists worked with the idea that ultimately all things are interrelated, was Paracelsus, to whom we have already referred.

To illustrate some features of the true world image as it is being completed and perfected with the aid of morphological methods, I submit three examples, one each from the following three types of complexes: a totality of material bodies and their common features; a totality of certain phenomena of the outer world; a group of concepts.

The totality of regular bodies with equal plane polygonal surfaces. Using the morphological method of total field coverage we shall show in the next chapter that there are five and only five regular geometrical bodies with flat surfaces, and we shall investigate in how many ways they can be constructed. Extrapolating and generalizing the results thus gained opens up rather surprising new vistas concerning practical and theoretical applications.

The totality of energy transformations. In order to make the most effective use of various occurrences of energy for industrial, commercial, and scientific projects we must not only know how many types of energy exist in nature but also how and with what efficiency they can be transformed one into another. This problem will be discussed in Chapter 4.

A totality of evaluations. As a prosaic and even trivial problem, the proper solution of which requires some rather abstract knowledge, I mention the declaration of income tax. If one, as he should, wants to determine the absolute minimum of the tax he must pay, yet not conflict with the authorities, he must clearly understand the laws and study the often intricate regulations and instructions, as they are formulated and issued by the governmental bureaucrats. He must keep a multitude of circumstances in the proper perspective in order to decide on the most favorable alternative. Unfortunately, it is not just a matter of correctly completing the various forms the governmental revenue agents send out every year, but of keeping records of activities and receipts. In addition, well-considered, long-range planning is most important because, depending on the country, much may be saved in some instances by transferring property during one's lifetime to one's wife, children, or various nonprofit or profit enterprises (such as operate with a loss) or by changing legal residence. This is evidently a complex of problems, which can effectively and profitably be dealt with if one uses the morphological approach, since, obviously, all factors and relevant circumstances must be considered to determine the minimum tax payment that is compatible with the law of the land. Curiously enough, however, after looking around among my colleagues in many countries and for many years, I have come to suspect that few of them think or act morphologically, not even when this often rather important issue of taxes is at stake. Actually, not much else could have been expected, because at home and in both the lower schools and the university the future scientists probably never heard much about how to manage the problems of everyday living and even less about how to deal most effectively with taxes and financial investments. Many difficulties, for instance those that commonly arise when the breadwinner suddenly or prematurely dies, could certainly be avoided if at school, or within the family, important economic and legal principles and experiences had been discussed as a necessary corollary to professional education, and if every husband quite unemotionally educated his wife and children to be widow and orphans since death and taxes are the only certain things in life as the saying goes.

THE RARITY OF UNIVERSAL INVENTORS AND MEN OF RESEARCH

In the preceding we have mentioned three examples that were taken from various fields, and we have indicated that in all cases the morphological methods can be applied usefully and profitably. It has often been stated that it is no longer possible today to know all or even several fields of science well, let alone to contribute materially to their advancement. This erroneous belief, as well as the rather astounding fact that among men of research there are but a very few who can make discoveries and inventions in widely separate fields, proves that the majority of them are either quite incapable of thinking morphologically or they have not yet learned or been taught to view the world as a whole. Contrary to the currently entrenched idea that universality of knowledge is a thing of the past, those who can visualize the true world image will nevertheless be capable of successfully doing research on many diverse subjects. They will also succeed in producing discoveries and inventions that have escaped the specialists in all domains of human activity because such specialists lack that type of universal outlook which, as I hope to show, automatically leads to the recognition of entirely new insights.

In what follows we shall explain some of the methods developed by the morphological approach. These methods allow us in successive stages to construct an integrated picture of the world that will more faithfully represent the true, harmonious, and completely rounded out world image.

THREE CLASSES OF PROBLEMS

Before starting our discussion we must call attention to the following obvious point: Even with the aid of the morphological methods it is not possible to solve *all* problems without further preparation. It must nevertheless be stressed that the morphological approach always opens up new vistas. The chances for success in dealing with various situations can generally be weighed, if we visualize the characters of the tasks before us, and if we clearly keep in mind that these may be of three basic types.

Problems for Whose Solution Only Small Numbers of Pegs of Knowledge Need to be Known

We might, for instance, ask for the smallest box in which a given number of books of various sizes can be packed. Or, consider a tailor who must cut out of a roll of cloth, with a minimum loss of material, those pieces he needs for the construction of a specified garment. And another case: In analytical mechanics one analyzes the number of proper modes of oscillation of a compound pendulum whose characteristic property is that all parts making up the pendulum oscillate with the same frequency and in the same phases. This famous problem has been solved by mathematical physicists by means of the theory of simultaneous linear differential equations. One more mathematical example: There exists presumably a very definite number of proofs, distinctly different from one another, of Pythagoras' law that the square of the hypotenuse of a triangle with one right angle is equal to the sum of the squares over the cathetes. What is this number? Analogous problems are encountered if we ask for all of the possible mechanisms that may be used as drives for clocks and watches. Or again, we may be interested in all propulsive power plants that are activated by chemical energy. It would also be of considerable interest to present-day technology and science to survey the totality of possible pumps, of all conceivable telescopes and so on. All problems of this type, which involve only a finite number of known determining parameters, can in principle be solved strictly and unambiguously with the aid of morphological methods. These methods, when necessary, make use of all procedures previously developed by conventional science and technology. In addition, however, the morphological approach introduces its own characteristic generalizations and modes of attack which, when coupled with its uncompromising attitude toward prejudice, endow it with its peculiar power and efficiency.

Problems for Whose Solution Pegs of Knowledge Are Necessary That Are as Yet Unavailable

I here mention the common cold, cancer, and many other diseases, the causes of which we are largely in the dark. Likewise unknown to us are all the possible methods, excluding the use of drugs and hypnosis, that might solve the problem of how to fall asleep at will and how to wake up at predetermined hours, although this latter problem is easier of solution. Most importantly, what are the origins of all human aberrations, and how can we eliminate, sublimate, or control them? One of the simplest but apparently quite difficult tasks in this area is how we can persuade a chain-smoker to abandon a filthy habit disastrous to himself and inconsiderate toward others without taking recourse to force or dictation.

In physics the total number of possible elementary particles is still unknown, not to mention their detailed charactcristics, since we do not as yet possess the basic pegs of knowledge to deal with these problems a priori, and the experimental physicists have not given us enough observational data to allow us to place properly the elementary particles in our morphological world image and visualize the role they play in it.

In all of the above-mentioned cases the morphological outlook can guide us with hints the ordinary expert often fails to recognize. But the morphological approach cannot produce miracles either, as long as essential pegs of knowledge are missing.

Problems That Involve Great Numbers of Parameters

There are complexes of objects, of phenomena, and of concepts about which we may possess sufficiently accurate knowledge individually but whose numbers are so great that we are forced to rely on statistical and probabilistic considerations such as have been used in statistical mechanics, one of the most powerful disciplines of modern physics. Probability calculus, the theory of large numbers and fluctuations, also plays a most important role in all problems of insurance for health, life, accidents, theft, transport, and so on. The same is true for all of thc transactions that involve the stock exchange. Although one knows in principle the elements of reason, error, psychological aberrations, and the emotional panics that may seize the masses, the outcome is never certain because the exact interactions of the great number of elements involved cannot be predicted accurately, and statistical estimates must therefore be substituted in place of unambiguous deductions.

THE RANGE OF VALIDITY OF MORPHOLOGICAL
RESEARCH

Morphological thinking and procedure can be applied to all tasks whose inherent characteristics are communicable and about which men can talk, and agree or disagree. This transmission of information, emotional experiences, and concepts and ideas can be achieved through speaking, writing, and all sorts of gestures or by any means that acts on our senses. The morphological procedures, therefore, not only include those used in all of the sciences, but also roam domains far beyond these and engage the various arts as powerful means of communication among men.

Beyond communicable truth and information we also know of the existence of large complexes of incommunicable truth[2] into which we can penetrate but little. In doing this we are forced to start from very uncertain and diffuse boundaries of those domains where the motivations originate in the inner worlds of men and drive them to concrete acts and activities whose aspects become recognizable to others and therefore communicable from man to man, although seldom understandable.

In order to clarify these thoughts, attention must be called to the important and disconcerting fact that, in addition to the incommunicable truths locked up within the inner worlds of other individuals, there exist similar ones buried within us, which at times, or forever, we are unable to communicate to ourselves. Indeed, I cannot today relive some of the emotions I experienced as a child. This means that I am incapable of recommunicating these experiences to myself, although I clearly remember the circumstances and events involved and these events may actually have been of great importance in my life and in that of others. Unfortunately, these incommunicable aspects of life are among

---

[2] We must distinguish here also between *incommunicable truths* which, by no means known to us, can be transmitted from individual to individual, and *noncommunicable truths*, the communication of which among men is in principle possible, but which may in practice be impeded, intentionally or unintentionally, through the interference of certain physical or spiritual obstacles.

precisely those that are characteristic of the inner stature of men, and which most often lie at the root of their tragic aberrations, motivations, and actions.

Recapitulating, we may state that morphological research primarily strives to understand the basic aspects and essential developments among all material, phenomenological, and spiritual relationships insofar as they can be objectively formulated and transmitted from individual to individual. Finally, I wish to caution the reader that a study as it is presented in this book may not immediately be comprehended in all of its implications. On the other hand, I believe that everyone can understand some of the ideas advanced and put them to good use in his own life and work. I hope in particular that I have made enough suggestions which will enable every reader to do some discovering and inventing of his own, both on a modest and perhaps occasionally more ambitious scale and thus contribute to our progress in technology, natural and social science, and particularly to the building of a harmonious human society.

3

The Morphological Methods I:
The Method of
Systematic Field Coverage

The morphological method of field coverage, which we have already alluded to in the previous chapter, can always be applied usefully if a sufficient number of pegs of knowledge is available within the field to be explored. These pegs or fixed points may be facts or personal experiences as well as experiences of others. Likewise, the possession of devices, machines, instruments, books, objects of art, and generally knowledge of the laws of nature and man as formulated by physics, chemistry, biology, and psychology represents a multitude of pegs of knowledge. The method of complete field coverage allows us to find *all* of the solutions of any well-defined problem. Starting from known pegs of knowledge, infiltrating the surrounding fields, and using a sufficient number of *principles of thought*, we strive to discover new facts, formulate new problems, and if necessary invent and produce needed new materials, instruments, and procedures.

Some of the major elementary principles of thought that we need are based on our ability to count and recognize identities, equalities, differences and coincidences in time and space. Furthermore we demand unambiguity of all solutions we derive when using several different approaches. If we err on our various ways to reaching a given desired goal, and therefore arrive at contradictory results, we must not fail to search for all false steps and erroneous conclusions, as well as all factors and circumstances that might have been neglected or incorrectly evaluated. Furthermore, the morphologist must never lose sight of the *continuity* of all things, all phenomena and all concepts and mental outlooks. He knows that within the final and true world image everything is related to everything, and nothing can be discarded a priori as being unimportant. This idea leads to the unorthodox conclusion that even a poor device, instrument or machine, a discouraging experience or a bad man may in the end have some beneficial influence on the course of the world. The morphologist thus considers many aspects of life that others glibly dismiss. Pointedly expressed, he is the *specialist of the impossible*, who knows that it is exceedingly difficult to prove this or that feat to be strictly impossible. Provided that impossibility cannot be clearly demonstrated, he will persevere, even where all others have long since given up the effort. He will start where others have quit.

Generally, in all his explorations the morphologist strives for *complete field coverage*. This means that he will not be satisfied until he has found *all the solutions* to a given problem. In practical life, however, it may be of the greatest importance to search at least for *one or a few new facts*, or to make one or a few inventions, even if the more complete complexes of as yet unknown facts and inventions are beyond our reach. Professor John Strong of Johns Hopkins University in Baltimore, Maryland, who is also the vice president of our International Society for Morphological Research, calls this more limited type of procedure *Modest Morphology* (see page 259).

In the following we apply the method of complete field coverage to three types of cases, which involve first, interrelations among certain objects, second, interrelations among certain natural phenomena and third, the interplay of a number of abstract concepts.

First Application of the Method of Field Coverage: Aggregates of Objects

THE REGULAR POLYHEDRA

We treat here some aspects of the geometry of *solid bodies*, which refer to their *external shapes*. This means that we only consider structural features of the surfaces of these bodies, and we are not concerned with their interiors.

First we ask for the total number and character of those regular polyhedra whose surfaces are flat regular polygons. Our second problem then will be to find out in how many ways we can build up these polyhedra by starting from flat arrays of the necessary number of adjacent regular polygons. We shall also be interested in exploring the values for mathematical theory, educational purposes and possible practical applications of the results achieved.

A next step to be taken in our unrelenting use of the method of complete field coverage might concern itself with the totality of those semiregular polyhedra (Archimedes' bodies) whose surface elements are made up of a mixture of various types of flat regular polygons. Again the problem will suggest the multitude of plane arrangements of the proper number of regular polygons which, when folded up along the pairwise-held edges, will unambiguously lead to the construction of the desired polyhedra.

And finally we shall show in two separate sections of this book how the totality of the elements and their mutual relations in certain limited and well-defined complexes of natural phenomena and abstract concepts can be deduced.

We now proceed to analyze the possible multiplicity of the regular polyhedra whose surfaces are all flat regular polygons, that is either equilateral triangles and squares or equilateral pentagons, hexagons, septagons and so on (see Fig. 1).

In order to construct a regular polyhedron we must arrange the correct number of the proper flat polygons edge (K) to edge in a plane in such a way that, after folding them up along these

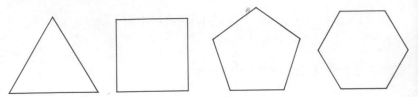

Fig. 1. *Regular polygons.*

edges, a definite part of space (the interior of the polyhedron) will be completely enclosed, and none of the surface elements will have been covered more than once. Applying the method of field coverage we proceed step by step and start with the simplest figure, the equilateral triangle (see Fig. 2). Laying only two triangles edge to edge and folding them through any angle along their common edge, no closed surface can ever result (Fig. 2a). In this way one cannot even obtain any spatial (spherical) angle. Such a solid angle can only result if we arrange at least three of the triangles edge to edge around a common corner (Fig. 2b). Folding them along the two common edges until the two peripheral ones through E meet we obtain a "paper bag" (three cornered dunce's hat) with an opening the shape of an equilateral triangle identical to those of the three "solid triangles," which we cut out of cardboard, for instance, and which constitute the faces of the bag (Fig. 2c). Only if we use four equilateral triangles and adjust them so as to form a larger triangle, double their linear size or four times their individual areas, and fold them along

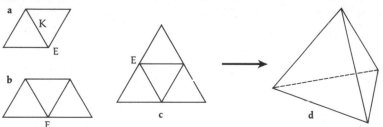

Fig. 2. *Construction of the tetrahedron by means of folding up four equilateral triangles arranged edge to edge in a plane. Not more than three triangles may share a common corner E.*

their mutual edges, will we obtain a first closed body, the *tetra-hedron* (Fig. 2d).

A second arrangement of the four triangles, that is, one in a straight line, adding one triangle either to the left or to the right of the one shown in Figure 2b can also be folded into complete tetrahedron. There are consequently *two plane arrangements* of four equilateral triangles, which are usable for the construction of a tetrahedron.

In review we state that the tetrahedron is a regular polyhedron whose six edges have the same length, and all angles, that is the twelve plane angles among themselves, as well as the six angles in the planes normal to the edges and the four solid angles with their apices at the corners, have respectively the same size.

We notice from Figure 2 that, no matter how we arrange the first three triangles edge to edge, they will always have one of their corners E in common. None of the corners of the fourth triangle must, however, come to be located on E; otherwise we would obtain a four-edged paper bag after folding up the plane arrangement properly, instead of the desired three-edged bag. It is obvious that by combining the mentioned two four-edged bags we may construct a regular polyhedron with eight equal triangles as their surfaces. This is the *octahedron*. If we draw the outlines

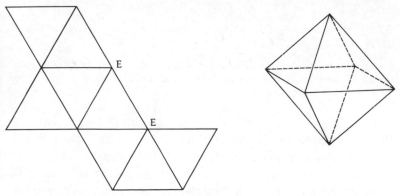

Fig. 3. Construction of an octahedron through folding up eight adjacent equilateral triangles along their mutual edges. Any of the common corners must not be shared by more than four triangles.

of the eight triangles in a suitable arrangement edge to edge on a piece of cardboard and cut out this complex with scissors, we can construct the octahedron by folding the cardboard along the seven edges, each of which is common to two of the triangles. One of the proper plane layouts is shown in Figure 3.

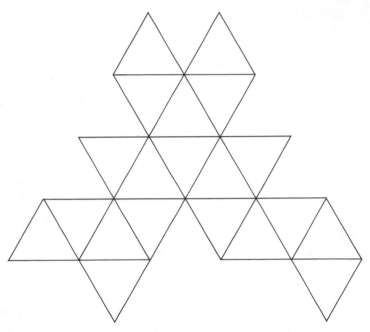

Fig. 4. *Construction of the icosahedron from an array of twenty properly arranged adjacent equilateral triangles. No corner point E must be shared by more than five triangles.*

In analogy to the statement made previously with regard to the construction of the tetrahedron, we have here encountered the restriction that not more than four of the equilateral triangles can share a common corner E, as shown in Figure 3. Should there exist a point E, shared by the corners of five triangles, the corresponding plane arrangement of the eight triangles cannot be used for the construction of an octahedron, but represents a pos-

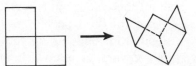

Fig. 5. Solid (spherical angle) defined by a bag of three paper squares.

sible element for composing a third regular polyhedron. It is this, the *icosahedron*, whose surface consists of twenty equilateral triangles. Therefore, if we start with five interconnected cardboard triangles around a common point E, and add fifteen more as shown in Figure 4, we may build an icosahedron by folding the twenty elements through the proper angles around their nineteen pairwise common edges.

Six equilateral triangles laid edge to edge around a common point E form a plane hexagon. This cannot be folded at all without distorting the plane, and it does not therefore represent an element suitable for the construction of a fourth polyhedron consisting of equilateral triangles. Thus there exist only three regular polyhedra, the tetrahedron, the octahedron, and the icosahedron, that can be built up with flat equilateral triangles as their surfaces.

Considering now the *square* as a building element we see that, just as in the case of the triangle, we need three squares in a plane, edge to edge and with one common corner E in order to produce a three-edged bag by folding this arrangement along the two pairs of common edges (see Fig. 5).

Since all angles, both those between the edges and those between the planes shown in Figure 5, are right angles, only one

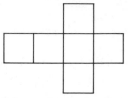

Fig. 6. Plane arrangement of six squares, which can be folded up to produce a cube.

single regular polyhedron, the *cube*, can be obtained by properly joining two identical "bags" of the type shown. There exist, obviously, no further possibilities for building up convex bodies whose surface elements are all squares. Again we inquire how the six cardboard squares can be arranged edge to edge in such a way that after folding them up through right angles a complete cube results. One of the possible ways of joining the squares for this purpose is shown in Figure 6.

We repeat that, with the squares as the prime elements of its surface, only one regular polyhedron, the cube, can be built up, because four squares edge to edge around a common corner E produce a larger flat square, which cannot be folded up without distorting the plane. Consequently no solid angle smaller than the half sphere can be obtained in this manner. Four squares edge to edge and with one common corner E therefore cannot be used for the construction of a cube or for any polyhedron different from the cube.

We now proceed with our complete field coverage by investi-

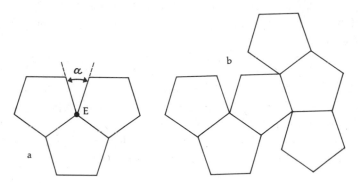

Fig. 7. *Successive composition of regular pentagons in a plane for the construction of a regular polyhedron, the dodecahedron.*

gating the regular bodies that can be built by using exclusively regular pentagons as their surface elements. Since each of the five angles of the pentagon has 108 degrees, three of them can be laid edge to edge around a common corner E, leaving an open angle

$\alpha = 360° - 324° = 36°$ as shown in Figure 7a. Folding the three pentagons up along the two pairwise, commonly held edges until the angle α is closed, we obtain a three-edged flat cup (or bowl), which may serve as the only possible triple element of pentagons for the construction of the dodecahendron. After proper folding of the six pentagons, as shown joined in Figure 7b, a rather artistic basket is produced. Putting two of these together so as to close all gaps we obtain a dodecahedron, that is a regular polyhedron with twelve flat regular pentagons as its surface elements. In other words we may combine two of the

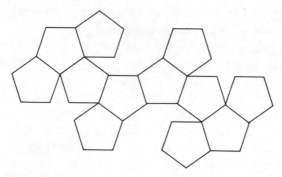

Fig. 8. A *plane layout of twelve pentagons edge to edge which may be folded up to produce a regular dodecahedron.*

partial arrangements of Figure 7b to form the total complex of the twelve pentagons shown in Figure 8, which after proper folding produces the complete dodecahedron. This is the only regular polyhedron which can be constructed with regular flat pentagons as its surface elements. Indeed, it is not possible to arrange more than three of the regular pentagons edge to edge around a common corner E, since this would necessarily lead to the overlapping of some of the surfaces. With the five regular bodies we have so far discussed, we have actually exhausted all the possibilities for construction of regular polyhedra. Already the next polygon, the hexagon, must be discarded as a possible "building stone," since three of them, arranged edge to edge and with one common

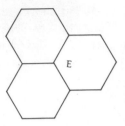

Fig. 9. *Three regular hexagons in the arrangement shown cover the plane around the common corner E completely.*

corner E, cover the plane around this corner completely. They cannot therefore be folded up to produce a solid angle smaller than the half sphere without being warped (see Fig. 9).

Proceeding further with our field coverage it is obvious that any attempt to arrange regular septagons, octagons and so on, respectively, edge to edge and around a common corner in a plane would lead to increasing areas of this plane being covered twice and successively more often. These higher order polygons therefore cannot be used for the construction of any further regular polyhedra. We have thus proved with the method of systematic field coverage that there exist only five regular polyhedra, that is,

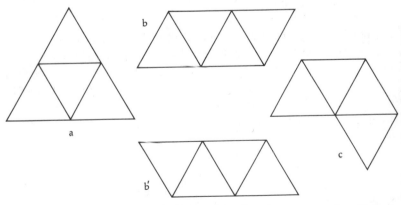

Fig. 10. *Construction of a tetrahedron from four interconnected equilateral triangles. The arrangement c cannot be used.*

the tetrahedron, the octahedron, the icosahedron, the cube, and the dodecahedron.

In continuation of our systematic inquiry we now ask in how many ways we can build up each of the five polyhedra by starting respectively with plane arrays of equilateral triangles, squares, and regular pentagons. These more difficult problems can again be solved in a straightforward way with the morphological method of complete field coverage. In fact we shall show that the *total number of possible plane arrangements* can in each case be found either through construction or dissection of the regular polyhedra.

SYSTEMATIC CONSTRUCTION AND DISSECTION

The Construction of the Tetrahedron

The four equilaterial triangles we need for the construction of a tetrahedron can be arranged usefully edge to edge in only three ways, as shown in Figures 10a, b and b'. The fourth arrangement, which is illustrated in Figure 10c, cannot be used for the buildup of a tetrahedron, since after folding it up along the internal edges, we obtain a four-edged bag or pyramid which represents one half of an octahedron.

Furthermore, since the array b' is the mirror image of the array b it cannot be counted as an independent solution to our problem. Indeed, if the layouts b and b' were cut out of a piece of cardboard, flipping b' over on its back would reveal it to be identical with the array b for purposes of construction. Thus there are just *two* independent plane arrangements of four equilateral tri-angles edge to edge that can be folded up to produce tetrahedra.

Dissection of the Tetrahedron

Starting from a complete tetrahedron, which is contstructed of cardboard, we must obviously slit it open along three edges in order to flatten it out into an interconnected flat array of four equilaterial triangles. There are three ways of locating this triple

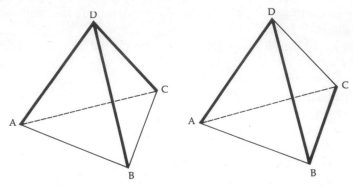

Fig. 11. *Usable ways of dissecting the tetrahedron along the heavily outlined edges for purposes of flattening it into an interconnected array of four equilateral triangles.*

cut, only two of which, however, lead to the desired result (see Fig. 11). The first possibility is to cut along the edges DA, DB, DC, starting from any arbitrary corner D. Flattening out the tetrahedron, the array (a) of Figure 10 is obtained. Secondly we can dissect along a zigzag path from A to D, D to B and B to C. This gives us the arrays b and b' of Figure 10. Finally we may cut open the edges A to B, B to C and C to A with the result that the triangle ABC falls out and leaves the rest of the tetrahedron intact as a three-edge bag. This last triple cut is therefore useless, since it does not allow us to flatten the tetrahedron into a plane arrangement.

In the preceding we have applied the method of field coverage to the processes of the construction and dissection of the tetrahedron, and we have shown that there exist only two independent plane arrays of four equilateral triangles laid edge to edge that can be folded into a complete tetrahedron. We now proceed to carry out the analogous analyses for the construction and dissection of a cube. Readers who intend to familiarize themselves more thoroughly with the application of the morphological methods might in the same way attempt to investigate the modes of construction and dissection of the octahedron, dodecahedron, and the icosahedron.

Construction of the Cube

Starting with plane arrangements of identical squares, it is obvious that two of them can be joined edge to edge in only one way.

A *third*, shaded square (Fig. 12) may be joined with the first two in the three ways shown. The two arrangements A_2 and A_3,

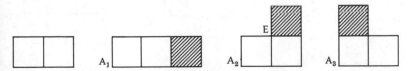

Fig. 12. *The three possible plane arrays of three squares joined edge to edge, which all may serve as parts for the construction of a cube.*

however, differ in no way from one another as concerns their usability as partial building elements for the construction of a cube. Because, if we either turn A_3 counterclockwise through a right angle around a vertical, or if we flip it on its backside, we can superimpose it exactly on A_2. In the following, therefore, we shall disregard all arrangements of squares that can be obtained by mirroring or rotation from arrays already chosen for the construction of the cube.

Adding a *fourth* square to the two arrays A_1 and A_2, we obtain the three arrays B_1, B_2 and B_3 from A_1, while A_2 leads to the new pattern B_4 and again to B_2 and B_3 (see Fig. 13).

Except for mirror images of B_2, B_3 and B_4 there exist no further new usable layouts of four squares, as can readily be proved by

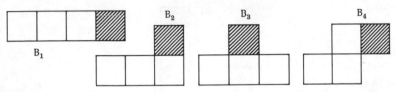

Fig. 13. *The four possible different plane arrangements of four squares joined edge to edge that may serve as partial sections for the construction of a complete cube.*

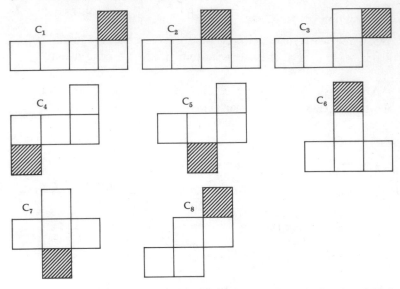

Fig. 14. *Plane arrangements of five squares edge to edge, which, when folded up, may serve as useful parts of a cube.*

investigating all of the complexes that result if we tentatively join a fourth square to *all* of the free edges of the arrays A_2 and A_3.

Adding a *fifth* (shaded) square respectively to B_1, B_2, B_3 and B_4, the eight basic patterns shown in Figure 14 result.

Starting from B_1, we obtain the arrangements C_1 and C_2. Adding a fifth square to different edges of B_2 will yield the patterns C_3, C_4 and C_5, all of them basically different from C_1 and C_2. The array B_3 plus an additional square will produce either C_6 or

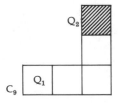

Fig. 15. *Arrangement of five squares that cannot be used for the desired type of construction of a cube.*

C_7, and finally, B_4 plus a fifth square results in the arrangement C_8. Further combinations of five squares edge to edge, which are different from C_1 to C_8 and after folding constitute a part of a cubic surface, cannot be found. This is again easily verified by tentatively joining respectively an additional square to all of the free edges of the arrays B_1 to B_4. For instance, the combination C_9, shown in Figure 15, which is obtained by adding a fifth square to B_2 is not usable for the construction of a cube, since after fold-

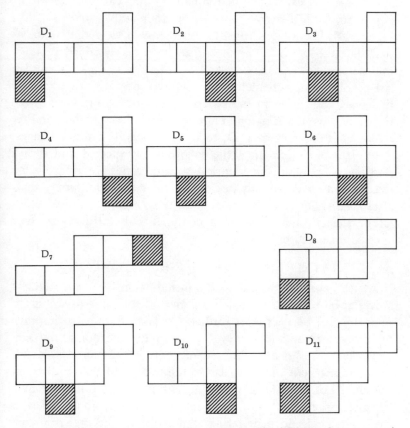

Fig. 16. Total number of all possible and mutually different plane arrays of six squares edge to edge, which, after folding along their five common edges, may each respectively serve for the construction of a complete cube.

ing the two "wings" along the four common internal edges, the two squares Q_1 and Q_2 will overlap each other on the "roof" of a cube, which is left with two open faces (vertical front and right side).

For the same reason five squares in a straight row are not admissible. Thus there remain only the patterns C_1 to C_8 that contain five squares edge to edge and that may serve as integral parts of a cube.

Adding the *sixth* and final square to the patterns shown in Figure 16, we first derive from C_1 the four usable arrays D_1, D_2, D_3 and D_4. Likewise, C_2 plus the sixth square yield the combinations D_5 and D_6; C_3 and another square properly added produce the patterns D_7, D_8, D_9, D_{10}; and C_8 plus a final square furnish a last possible arrangement that can be used for the construction of the cube and is different from all others. Starting from C_4, C_5, C_6, C_7, however, and adding one more square, no new combination results that is different from D_1 to D_{11} or from their mirror images.

We therefore can draw the following unexpected and rather startling conclusion. Six identical squares can be arranged edge to edge in *eleven*, and only in eleven plane geometrical arrays that, after folding up along those five edges common to pairwise adjacent squares, will produce a complete cube with every face covered once and only once.

ABBREVIATED METHOD OF FIELD COVERAGE

As we have emphasized in the introduction, the morphologist strives at all times, if possible, to derive *all* solutions to any given problem. But he goes even further. He also attempts to improve his procedures and to achieve optimum understanding and efficiency by means of exploring not just one but all conceivable avenues and methods that will lead to the totality of the solutions in question. For teaching purposes in particular it is often desirable to present the students with the shortest possible proofs and with the most lucid and penetrating arguments. In the presently considered case of the construction of a cube from a plane interconnected array of six squares we may, for instance, shorten the derivation of the results arrived at in the preceding as follows:

We start from a few pegs of knowledge which are geometrically evident from the beginning. *First*, we see that we cannot usefully arrange more than three squares edge to edge around a common corner E (see Fig. 12), because four squares with a mutually held corner E cannot be folded along the commonly held edges without distorting the plane. *Second*, the "angle iron" formation C_9 of Figure 15 cannot be admitted in any of the arrangements for which we are looking. And *third*, not more than four of the six squares may be joined along a straight line. Otherwise, after folding we would obtain double coverage of one or of two faces of the cube. Therefore only two, three or four squares may be arranged along a straight line.

Starting from *four squares along a straight line* and adding a fifth and a sixth square, we readily obtain the patterns D_1 to D_6. Any further useful arrays cannot be produced, if we remember that the two additional squares must be joined laterally to the rectangular chain of the first four squares.

Next we start with *three squares arranged along a straight line*. We may first add the remaining three squares as a block, which is identical with the first block of three. This produces only the arrangement D_7. We can, however, separate the additional three squares into two groups of one and two. Adding these properly to the linear block of the first three squares we successively arrive at the arrangements D_8, D_9 and D_{10}.

And finally, starting from a *block of only two squares*, we must of necessity add the four remaining squares in two separate blocks of two, since we have already discussed all available arrangements that contain linear blocks of three squares. As a result of the only possible combination of the three blocks of two squares, the last pattern D_{11} is obtained. We have thus shown again that there exist *eleven*, and only eleven, plane arrangements of six squares laid edge to edge that satisfy our requirements for the construction of the cube.

Dissection of the Cube

In chemistry, and particularly in organic and in biochemistry, the structure of complex molecules is being investigated by means of both analysis and synthesis. Actually the method of successively splitting the large molecules apart proved most successful in the mentioned disciplines. In most cases the synthesis of the substances involved is much more difficult, and in many instances has not yet been achieved. In contradistinction to the greater advantages of the methods of dissection in chemistry it is rather surprising that for the problems related to the structure of the cube the step by step synthesis furnishes us the desired characteristics of the essential "building stones" faster and more comprehensibly than the processes of dissection, which we are now going to discuss.

If we think of flattening out a cardboard cube into a plane array of six interconnected squares, we must cut the cube along seven of its edges and fold it open by turning its faces each respectively through a right angle around one of the five pairwise common edges. The total number of plane arrays that can be obtained in this manner may be found either through an examination one by one of all of the possible sevenfold cuts or by an analysis of the possible relative locations of the five edges around which five squares must be turned, each through a right angle, to come to lie in the same plane as the sixth square. Here we have chosen to analyze the plane patterns of six interconnected squares that are obtained if we cut the cube in all possible ways along seven of its edges, this being probably the simplest means of analysis by dissection.

The determination of the totality of all possible different plane arrangements of six squares that can be obtained by flattening out the cube, after a minimum number of seven cuts along its edges has been made, is a very tedious process; indeed *all* possible sevenfold cuts must be carefully investigated in order not to overlook any of the desired plane arrays. I must leave it to the younger generation of morphologists to discover procedures of dissection

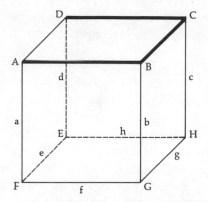

Fig. 17. *The first necessary step for the dissection and the flattening out of a cube, which is constructed of cardboard for instance, into an interconnected plane array of six squares involves a minimum (and a maximum) of three cuts along the edges of any one of the six square faces. The cuts along AB, BC, and CD are heavily outlined.*

that are simpler and more straightforward than the one I am presenting here.

We first observe that the application of cuts along any seven edges of the (cardboard) cube will either completely sever one of the squares, or we shall find at least one square face that has been cut along three of its edges (horseshoe cut).

Since cuts that make the cube fall apart into two or more pieces are of no interest to us, we begin the process of dissection with one of the unavoidable threefold horseshoe-shaped cuts around an arbitrary face, say ABCD in Figure 17. All cuts made are marked by heavy lines.

The edge AD must remain intact throughout, since otherwise the cube would fall apart. For the final dissection of the cube to allow us to flatten it out, four more cuts must be properly made. We have the choice of four vertical edges, $AF = a$, $BG = b$, $CH = c$, $DE = d$, and of four horizontal edges, $EF = e$, $FG = f$, $GH = g$ and $HE = h$. In order to be able to flatten out the cardboard cube we must thus cut four of the eight edges just mentioned. Mathematicians will notice immediately that this can be done in seventy different ways [the number of combinations of four edges among the total number of the eight available edges a, b, c, d, e, f g, h, is in fact equal to the so-called binomial coefficient $\binom{8}{4} = \dfrac{8 \cdot 7 \cdot 6 \cdot 5}{1 \cdot 2 \cdot 3 \cdot 4} = 70$]. Using the method of field coverage, which is in this case equivalent to the enumeration of a finite number of possibilities, we can formulate the seventy possible combinations of four different elements immediately. I again emphasize that for our purposes we are actually forced to do that in order not to miss any of the plane arrays of six squares, interconnected edge to edge, that can be used for the reconstruction of the cube through the process of successive folding of the elements involved. For convenience we group the various combinations of the four cuts, chosen from the total possible eight cuts, according to the number of vertical edges (a, b, c, d) contained in it. We thus arrive at the following scheme of the seventy possible fourfold cuts.

The combinations which contain:

Four Vertical Cuts: 1. (a, b, c, d)

Three Vertical Cuts: ✕ 2. (a, b, c, f)
                                             ✕ 3. (a, b, c, g)
                                                 4. (a, b, c, h)
                                                 5. (a, b, c, e)

                                         — 6. (f, b, c, d)
                                         — 7. (g, b, c, d)
                                         — 8. (h, b, c, d)
                                         — 9. (e, b, c, d)

                                        10. (a, f, c, d)
                                        11. (a, g, c, d)
                                    ✕ 12. (a, h, c, d)
                                    ✕ 13. (a, e, c, d)

                                   — 14. (a, b, f, d)
                                   — 15. (a, b, g, d)

— 16. (a, b, h, d)
— 17. (a, b, e, d)

Two Vertical Cuts:

× 18. (a, b, e, f)
   19. (a, b, e, g)
   20. (a, b, e, h)
× 21. (a, b, f, g)
× 22. (a, b, f, h)
   23. (a, b, g, h)

   24. (a, c, e, f)
   25. (a, c, e, g)
× 26. (a, c, e, h)
× 27. (a, c, f, g)
   28. (a, c, f, h)
   29. (a, c, g, h)

× 30. (a, d, e, f)
× 31. (a, d, e, g)
— 32. (a, d, e, h)
   33. (a, d, f, g)
   34. (a, d, f, h)
— 35. (a, d, g, h)

   36. (b, c, e, f)
× 37. (b, c, e, g)
— 38. (b, c, e, h)
× 39. (b, c, f, g)
   40. (b, c, f, h)
— 41. (b, c, g, h)

— 42. (b, d, e, f)
— 43. (b, d, e, g)
— 44. (b, d, e, h)
— 45. (b, d, f, g)
— 46. (b, d, f, h)
— 47. (b, d, g, h)

— 48. (c, d, e, f)
— 49. (c, d, e, g)
— 50. (c, d, e, h)
— 51. (c, d, f, g)
— 52. (c, d, f, h)
— 53. (c, d, g, h)

One Vertical Cut:

54. (a, e, f, g)
55. (a, e, f, h)
56. (a, e, g, h)
57. (a, f, g, h)

58. (b, e, f, g)
59. (b, e, f, h)
60. (b, e, g, h)
61. (b, f, g, h)

— 62. (c, e, f, g)
— 63. (c, e, f, h)
— 64. (c, e, g, h)
— 65. (c, f, g, h)

— 66. (d, e, f, g)
— 67. (d, e, f, h)
— 68. (d, e, g, h)
— 69. (d, f, g, h)

No Vertical Cut: × 70. (e, f, g, h)

It is seen immediately that certain combinations of cuts are located geometrically in symmetrical positions relative to the original "horseshoe cut" AB, BC, CD. In every such case only one of these combinations needs to be analyzed since the other will not lead to any new plane arrangement of interconnected squares that can be folded up into a cube. For instance, the fourfold cuts in the group 6 to 9 are in this sense equivalent to those from 2 to 5, since the cut along the edge (a), which is contained in all of the latter combinations has been replaced by the cut along (d), which with respect to the horseshoe ABCD is located symmetrically to (a). The same holds true for the group of fourfold cuts 14 to 17 whose cut (b) is symmetrical to the cut (c) contained in the combinations 10 to 13. A minus sign (—) in front of the number of the respective fourfold-cut designation thus indicates that this combination need not be investigated further (for instance the numbers 6, 7, 8, 9 and 14, 15, 16, 17) since an equivalent one has already been analyzed.

We notice furthermore that each of the complexes of cuts 48 to 53 lies symmetrically to one of the complexes 18 to 23, for instance (c, d, e, f) to (a, b, e, h). The same is true for the combinations 24 to 29 on the one hand and 42 to 47 on the other hand. Other symmetrical pairs are (a, d, e, f) and (a, d, e, h); (a, d, f, g) and (a, d, g, h); (b, c, e, f) and (b, c, e, h); and (b, c, f, g) and (b, c, g, h). And finally we need not separately consider the combinations 62 to 65 and 66 to 69 since these two groups are equivalent to the groups 58 to 61 and 54 to 57. There remain thus for further analysis only 38 of the total number of 70 groups of cuts. Among these the crossed off combinations (×) 2, 3, 12, 13, 18, 21, 22, 26, 27, 30, 31, 37, 39, and 70 are unusable because they correspond to the cases in which one or two of the square faces of the cube would be completely severed from the rest.

The remaining 24 nontrivial combinations of cuts lead to the following plane arrays of interconnected squares as they are shown and designated in Figure 16. The combination of cuts 56 produces the pattern D_1; 28, 55 and 59 produce D_2 when the cube is flattened out. Numbers 10, 54 and 60 each give the array D_3; 34 and 57 lead to D_4; 4 and 58 to D_5; 1, 40 and 61 to D_6; 33 to D_7; 20 and 25 to D_8; 5, 29 and 36 to D_9; 11, 19 and 23 to D_{10} and finally 24 to D_{11}.

Working with the method of field coverage in three distinctly different ways, that is applying it twice to the construction and once to the dissection of the cube, we have therefore proved that there exist exactly *eleven plane arrangements of squares* laid edge to edge that can be folded up to produce a complete cube. This

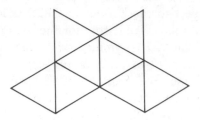

Fig. 18. An arrangement of eight equilateral triangles which is different from that shown in Fig. 3 and which can readily be folded up along the internal edges to produce an octahedron.

result probably will surprise even those mathematicians and topologists who possess profound geometrical vision.

Using analogous procedures of the construction and dissection of the remaining regular polyhedra all of the plane arrays of equilateral triangles and pentagons can be found that may be folded up successfully into complete octahedra, icosahedra and dodecahedra. I leave these rather more difficult problems to the younger morphologists, as well as to possible critics and disbelievers, as useful exercises for their geometrical vision and imagination. To

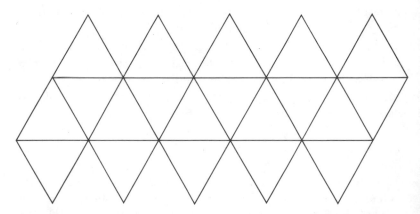

Fig. 19. An arrangement of twenty equilateral triangles which is different from that shown in Fig. 4 and which can be folded up to produce a complete icosahedron.

accompany the future students of the morphological approach on their way, however, I add Figures 18, 19 and 20, which, in addition to the arrangements shown in Figures 3, 4 and 8, illustrate other arrays of equilateral triangles and regular pentagons that can be used for the construction of octahedra, icosahedra and dodecahedra.

In California, where we live, milk and many fruit juices are being sold in cubic or prismatic waxed carton containers. During various stays in Switzerland we noticed that tetrahedral cartons or so-called tetrapacks are being used there for the purpose. My wife pointed out to the managers of some of the Swiss supermarkets that the tetrapacks not only cannot be stacked properly in the refrigerators, where space may often be at a premium, but that, as we frequently observed, the users spill parts of their contents on pouring from or on piercing the containers. Furthermore, the tetrapacks are being shipped in cylindrical wire crates which cannot be properly and stably braced against each other and

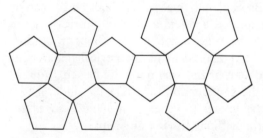

Fig. 20. *An arrangement of twelve regular pentagons which can be folded up along the commonly held edges to produce a complete dodecahedron.*

which leave between them much unused space. I therefore asked one of the major suppliers of tetrapacks just what advantages could compensate for the many shortcomings mentioned. Of particular interest to me was that part of his answer revolved around the claim that patterns of six interconnected squares could not be cut out from large cartons without considerable loss of material. He was under the impression that such losses could only be minimized if one used the pattern b of Figure 10 for the construction of the tetrahedron, which led them to the choice of the tetrapack. The engineers and designers who had occupied themselves with the problems of packing seemed to have overlooked the fact that several of the patterns D_1 to D_{11}, which can be used for the construction of cardboard cubes (and in some cases for rectangular prisms), may very well be joined in arrays that cover large parts of plane surfaces continuously. This is true for instance for the crosslike pattern D_8 as demonstrated in Figures 21a and 21b. The patterns D_7 and D_{11} (of Fig. 16) can even be joined continuously to cover long strips of constant widths equal to two and three times the width of the elementary squares.

Generally the question may be asked which of the patterns D_1 to D_{11} of Figure 16 can be joined in arbitrary numbers so as to cover a plane surface without leaving any gaps, and furthermore, in how many ways this can be done. While all of these problems can be solved through a systematic application of the morphological method of total field coverage, it might actually be difficult to develop precise mathematical methods and theorems that could give us the desired answers and results directly. For purposes of acquainting themselves with the various procedures involved, those who are interested in morphological research might investigate the problem of how many of the flattened out arrangements needed for the construction of octahedra, dodecahedra, and icosahedra can be joined together continuously so as to cover large plane surfaces without leaving any gaps.

In this connection the further question arises as to which of the regular and semiregular polyhedra, singly or in mixed groups, can be stacked so as to fill large parts of three-dimensional space completely. Answers to this query are obviously of importance in crystallography and in chemistry, where we deal with homogeneous spatial arrangements of identical elementary cells containing one or more types of molecules.

With respect to education, considerations of the type presented in the preceding are of interest because they help to sharpen and to develop the spatial intuition of the student. One might in fact

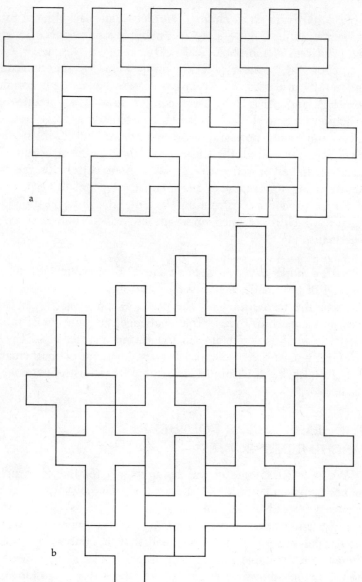

Fig. 21. *Continuous coverage of the plane by means of interlacing the cross-like patterns D₆ of six squares that individually can be folded up to cubes.*

wish to start with small children and let them play with toys such as jigsaw puzzles, which involve and bring into evidence some of the principles of morphological field coverage in disguise.

Among the possible practical applications of the procedures and results discussed, the question of possible patterns for floor coverings and other decorative designs as well as architectural structures in general come to mind. Related studies have not only led to interesting new and artistic solutions, but have in many cases also minimized the time and labor of construction. For instance, it has proved easier to lay a floor pattern of the type shown in Figures 21a and b, using entire crosses of the type of D_6 of Figure 16 as the construction elements, than to join individual squares, which if not lined up accurately, will be judged as sloppy workmanship.

As we hope to have demonstrated, the application of the method of systematic field coverage not only opens up new vistas for both the theoretical and the practical morphologist. In addition, problems come to light that challenge the professional mathematician and topologist and in the future may result in the development of entirely new and fruitful branches of mathematics.

Before leaving this subject, two more brief suggestions may be made.

THE SEMIREGULAR POLYHEDRA (ARCHIMEDES' BODIES)

We now relax some of our requirements for the construction of polyhedra and admit two different regular polygons as surface elements instead of only one. For instance we ask if equilateral triangles and squares can be combined for the buildup of a semiregular polyhedron. Also we shall find that, in contradistinction to the elements suitable for the regular polyhedra, regular hexagons now become admissible inasmuch as they can, for instance, be combined with regular pentagons for the buildup of an Archimedes type body. Proceeding still further, we may try to use three or more regular polygons as possible plane surface elements. The question consequently arises of how many semiregular polyhedra exist. The answer to this question can again be obtained through a systematic application of the method of complete field coverage to the construction and dissection of the bodies involved. We indicate briefly how one might proceed, but we must leave the completion of the entire complex of inquiries to the interested reader.

Severing the corners of any of the five regular polyhedra by symmetrically applied plane cuts, semiregular polyhedra may be constructed. For instance, if we subject the tetrahedron to this operation, we first obtain a polyhedron with four equilateral triangles and four not equilateral hexagons (see Fig. 22). The

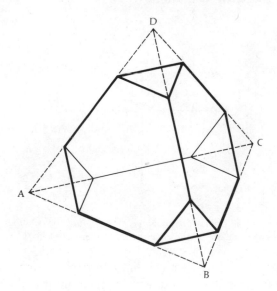

Fig. 22. *Starting from a tetrahedron (A, B, C, D), an Archimedes type semi-regular polyhedron with four equilateral triangles and four regular hexagons as its surfaces is obtained by severing the four corners of the tetrahedron through the application of four symmetrical plane cuts at the proper depths. Cutting still deeper until the corners of the newly cut triangles meet, an octahedron results.*

latter four polygons become regular, however, if we proceed with our cuts to the proper depths at which the Archimedes type body with four equilateral triangles and four regular hexagons emerges. Cutting still deeper until the edges of the original tetrahedron are cut exactly in half, a regular octahedron results.

Start From a Central Frame of Straight Lines

In order to construct any polyhedron we must naturally operate in three dimensions. We can thus start from a framework of at least three straight lines that do not all lie in the same plane. For instance these lines may all pass through the same point O, and the angles between them must preferably all be equal in order to allow us to construct regular or semiregular polyhedra by a system of planes associated in a symmetrical way with the lines.

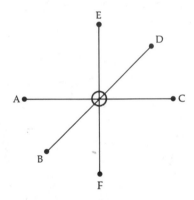

Fig. 23. Rectangular framework of three straight lines, which may serve as a base for the construction of the octahedron and for the cube.

We start with three straight lines through a comon point O (see Fig. 23). Since the angles between them must all be the same, they are of necessity all right angles. At equal distances from O we then mark on the three lines the six points, A, B, C, D, E and F. We then lay planes through those eight triplets of points (A, B, E), (A, B, F), etc., which do not lie in the original three planes defined by the three axes, and we obtain an *octahedron* as the space enclosed by these eight planes. If on the other hand we visualize the six planes through the points A to D, which lie normal to three straight lines of the rectangular framework, we obtain a cube as the enclosed space.

For the construction of the tetrahedron we need four straight lines through a point O with all angles between them respectively equal, and so forth for the dodecahedron and the icosahedron.

If we wish to construct semiregular polyhedra, we must investigate all the structures enclosed by various groups of planes, some of them at right angles and others obliquely oriented relative to a suitable symmetrical framework of straight lines that pass through a central point O and on which points A, B, C, D, etc., are marked off in groups at equal distances from O.

Attention should here be called to the fact that some of these problems have been solved elegantly in the more or less recent past with the aid of powerful mathematical tools such as the Galois group theory, general algebra and topology, but many analogous problems still await their solution through strictly formalized treatment.

As one of the best and longest known quantitative laws about polyhedra we must not fail to mention Euler's theorem which says that if e, s and c are respectively the total number of edges, surfaces and corners (or vertices) of a polyhedron, the following relation holds: $c + s = e + 2$. Thus, for the tetrahedron $s = 4$, $c = 4$ and $e = 6$; or for the icosahedron $s = 20$, $c = 12$ and $e = 30$. Euler's theorem may be proved in various ways by making use of the method of systematic field coverage. Actually, as far as I know, no proof at all has as yet been given which, methodologically, may not be classed as being of this type.

Summing up, we may say that the method of systematic field coverage we have applied in the preceding to the regular polyhedra as a totality of a limited number of objects always promises to lead to useful results and to open up new and unexpected vistas. We call attention once more to our suggestions concerning some practical and artistic uses of our results on the construction of regular polyhedra to a variety of problems in design, architecture and optimum packing of goods. Furthermore, the resulting challenges to abstract mathematics should not be forgotten. We shall show in the following that a similar broadening of our outlook on many other phases of human activities can be gained through the application of the morphological method of field coverage to a number of specific problems.

Second Application of the Method of Field Coverage: Interrelations Among Phenomena; Integral Engineering

In the preceding section we have acquainted ourselves with an application of the morphological method of field coverage to some of the characteristics of a limited totality of special objects, the regular polyhedra. We now turn our attention to the interrelations among certain groups of natural phenomena.

One of the classical examples for the application of the method of field coverage to the exploration of the general characteristics of natural phenomena was given by the great English physicist Michael Faraday (1791–1867). Practically his whole life was dedicated to research on the interrelations among these phenomena. As a consequence of his persevering efforts he discovered before all the law of electrical induction, that is of the effects that result from the interaction of motion, magnetic fields and electrical currents. He further investigated the relation between electrical and chemical phenomena and formulated his fundamental electrochemical equivalence law. And finally he found the magneto-optical effect and many other associative actions among the various phenomena of nature. These extraordinary achievements of Faraday's—with which he created not only the foundations for electrical engineering and for electrochemistry, but also for classical physics and chemistry in general—unfortunately cannot be further elaborated here. Those who wish to learn more about the life and work of this unique man of science can only be advised "to study the master," that is for instance Faraday's diaries and his semipopular writings.

A further outstanding example of a systematic search for mutual interrelations among all physical and chemical phenomena may of course be found in the Periodic System of the Chemical Elements, as it was established by Dimitri Mendeleev (1834–1907). Here we cannot go into any further details either since the reader may find all of the pertinent historical and scientific data, as well as excellent accounts of the far reaching and profound influence of Mendeleev's discovery on modern science and technology in the existing literature.

Faraday and Mendeleev, as well as the men mentioned previously (see p. 34 of the German edition) may in many ways be considered as the predecessors of the morphological approach. Their ways of thought and of procedure unquestionably moved within the general universe of discourse I have proposed to call the morphological world image, although they occupied themselves only with partial aspects of this image and apparently made no attempt or did not think of developing and systematically formulating the various morphological methods of discovery, invention and research.

In order to help the reader visualize the whole breadth and depth of the morphological approach we shall now discuss some examples which will demonstrate how the interrelations among groups of objects, among natural phenomena and among ideas and concepts can be explored in their integrated totality. Considerations concerning the construction of certain classes of instruments and machines serve admirably for this purpose. If I choose here in particular to consider the construction and the operation of telescopes, I hope that no one will accuse me of unduly promoting one of my professions, since the problems to be discussed have been of very particular interest to me as an astrophysicist.

TELESCOPES

Our friend the man in the street and even many of my colleagues in disciplines other than physics and astronomy will probably incredulously shake their heads if I claim that among the optical and the radio-telescopes that are in use today probably none is being operated at more than 50 per cent efficiency as far as its scientific use is concerned. I should even say that some among them, and especially a few of the most expensive and well-known ones, have hardly yielded more than 10 per cent of the results that might have been achieved in principle. The reasons for these regrettable facts may be found in various circumstances. We shall enumerate a few of the responsible causes that become apparent if we avail ourselves of the morphological approach towards a complete field coverage of those relevant phenomena and technical aspects that must never be lost sight of if we wish to construct telescopes that will produce the sought for scientific results at optimum efficiency, provided they are operated and controlled by astronomers who are free of stifling prejudices and are not driven to destructive behaviour caused by being the slaves of various mental aberrations. To give the particular complex of ideas and procedures we are going to discuss a name, we propose to call it *Integral Engineering*, which in short means integral planning, analysis, construction and operation of various types of apparatus, instruments and machines. It should here be mentioned that integral engineering probably shares many of its aspects with *systems engineering*, but I think it involves features that are much more general.

Applying the method of morphological field coverage we move from one reasonably well-established peg of knowledge to other pegs, thereby traversing as yet unknown fields, which need to be explored. But we can in principle start anywhere, and in our case we chose to begin with the individual who conceives of the necessity of some particular telescope and who plans and initiates its construction.

The Initiator

At this starting point already we become aware of a multitude of circumstances which largely determine the outcome of whether or not the intended telescope can become optimally effective, or whether it will be doomed to an existence of relative uselessness. For example, a complete failure may be in the cards from the beginning in a case where the ruler or a powerful political hierarchy in this or that country acquires an instrument solely for reasons of prestige, and in the end it is not being used or even installed for many years, or ever, because of the nonavailability of the necessary experts or because of personal rivalries among them. Such for instance is the case with one of the largest and finest Schmidt telescopes, which in a certain country remains in its original shipping cases. More often than most people would believe, however, the same fate has been suffered by other instruments, which were constructed in temporary bursts of enthusiasm by professionals or by groups among the ten thousands of amateurs in the many countries of the world and have never been operated in any reasonable or useful manner.

It of course may also happen that the initiator cannot be blamed at all, since he may pass away before the completion of his telescope. This in some way was the case at the Palomar Mountain Observatory, whose initiator, Dr. George Ellery Hale, excepting the 18-inch Schmidt telescope, did not live to see the 200-inch Hale telescope and the 48-inch Schmidt telescope put in operation. Actually, Dr. L. M. Humason, now in retirement, and the present writer are the only surviving members of a group of about ten who originally planned, constructed and operated the 200-inch Hale reflector and the three Schmidt telescopes (8-inch, 18-inch and 48-inch) associated with it, as well as the various installations on Palomar Mountain and at the Astrophysics Laboratory of the California Institute of Technology in Pasadena. World War II unfortunately interfered with and retarded the completion of the two largest Palomar telescopes by from six to eight years, and it is therefore not surprising that with the passing of the original planners and operators, all sorts of errors were made, and view points were adopted that did not conform with the originally set high standards and goals.

Generally speaking we expect of the initiator of any astronomical project that he clearly realize the basic scientific goals which are to be achieved with the aid of any planned telescopes and auxiliary devices and that he himself, possibly with the assistance of competent collaborators, know how to finance the whole under-taking and how to carry out its construction. It must be empha-sized in this connection that Dr. George Ellery Hale (1868–1938), founder of the Mount Wilson and Palomar Observatories as well as of the California Institute of Technology, was in the sense stated a truly unique person, a top scientist and ideal administra-tor. His methods and his successes in securing the funds necessary for the construction of the Palomar Observatory are classical and nothing short of miraculous. The introduction to his article "The Possibility of Large Telescopes," which appeared in the April, 1928, issue of *Harper's* magazine, probably represents, word for word, the most lucrative sentence ever written in the history of man. It says simply: "Like buried treasures, the outposts of the universe have beckoned to the adventurous from immemorial times."

The story goes that the directors of the Rockefeller Foundation in New York read only this one sentence and immediately in-formed Dr. Hale that they were putting at his disposal six million dollars for the construction of a giant telescope (the present 200-inch Palomar reflecting Hale Telescope).

The Location of a Telescope

Qui a le choix a l'embarras. Today we actually already have the choice of several possibilities. We can choose to install our telescope on the surface of the earth, on high-flying balloons, on sounding rockets, on manned or unmanned artificial satellites which circle the Earth and on unmanned space ships; and soon we shall be in a position to install instruments on the Moon, the advantages and disadvantages of which are being studied inten-sively by the LIL Committee (Lunar International Laboratory) of the International Academy of Astronautics.

For the solution of certain problems in astronomy and astro-physics the choice of the location of the observing instruments is practically unambiguous. For instance, if one wishes to study the far ultraviolet and the X-ray and Gamma-ray spectra of certain cosmic objects, one must observe them from heights above several hundred kilometers; at lower levels no recordings of these types of rays can be obtained, since the denser atmosphere absorbs them completely. On the other hand, if one is interested in infrared spectra, the alternative between balloons on the one hand and rockets, artificial satellites and space capsules on the other hand must be carefully considered. In particular the relative costs involved for the achievement of the results to be expected enter as a major item in this type of project. Large balloons can indeed lift more than a ton of payload to heights of 30 kilometers and more. Proper instruments carried aloft by such balloons can therefore effectively record all infrared radiations, since water vapour and ozone, which make the lower strata of the atmosphere opaque in these wave length ranges, exist in high altitudes only in negligible concentrations. In this connection we remember the following instance. The well-advertised spaceship *Mariner II*, for instance, was launched on December 14, 1962, in the direction of the planet Venus, which it passed six months later at a distance of 35,000 kilometers, from where it relayed back to the Earth information about the composition and the physical characteristics of the planet's atmosphere. The messages transmitted were rather difficult of interpretation and the funds expended were enormous. Professor John Strong of Johns Hopkins University in Baltimore (who is also vice president of the Society for Morphological Research) in 1964 observed Venus with instruments borne aloft by a giant balloon. He came to the conclusion that the upper atmosphere of Venus contains microscopic crystals of ice in great concentrations and that, in particular, the surface temperature of the planet is probably considerably lower than the 400° Centigrade which had been obtained from the analysis of the data supplied by *Mariner II*. What I wanted to stress here specifically, however, is the fact that the investment in Strong's balloon, his telescope (which was recovered) and the funds expended by him in gathering an extended series of relevant observational data amounted to considerably less than 1 per cent of the costs lavished on the *Mariner II* experiment. (The associated problem of whether or not the great costs can be justified on the basis of engineering know-how gained must of course be analyzed in addition if we are concerned with the over-all aspects of integral engineering and science of the project in question).

In the following we shall restrict ourselves to the discussion of the various factors that must be carefully considered if we are to succeed in the satisfactory construction and operation of a conventional type telescope with a minimum expenditure of manpower and funds. The location to be chosen for any telescope to be installed on the surface of the Earth can only be reasonably decided upon if we first make observations and tests concerning the following aspects of the "sky" at any of the sites considered.

To start with, we must know from the meteorologists how many nights a year, on the average, are clear or only partly cloudy. This information alone, however, will be decisive only for small telescopes of short focal length and for certain types of programs, such as the search for supernovae. Even a clear night, but with quite violent winds or peculiar turbulent disturbance in some strata of the atmosphere, may prove to be quite unusable when working with one of the giant telescopes. Indeed, the so-called "seeing," that is the "scintillations" of the stars may be so bad that their images on the photographic plates or other recorders will appear as "potatoes," that is not as pointlike sharp images, but smeared out over large areas. Also of prime importance is what astronomers now call the "night sky glow," or the permanent aurora. Because of this light, which may vary considerably in intensity, the night sky is never really "black." (Nights become much blacker under heavy cloud covers and, of course, really black in closed rooms.) The sky glow is due to the emission of both spectral lines and bands, as well as some continuous radiation from atoms, molecules and radicals in the ionosphere, where these particles are being continuously excited by mutual collisions, by the incoming light and electron streams from the Sun, the so-called solar wind, and by the cosmic rays, interstellar atomic rays and so on. In great northern and southern latitudes, as we approach the two magnetic poles of the Earth, the more local polar auroras may at times become so excessively bright that astronomical observations of cosmic objects are impossible.

Avoidable in principle but disastrous in practice are those blunders in planning that in the end impede or even may completely stop the observations at observatories located in the vicinity of large cities or other brightly lit complexes of human activities. Such centers not only illuminate the atmosphere, but they go at it with a vengeance inasmuch as they contribute at the same time to the enrichment of the air with all sorts of aerosols, smoke, dust and smog, which in turn efficiently scatters the light from the cities in all directions. A considerable number of observatories have become useless for this very reason.

Thought must also be given the ease of access to an observatory site as well as the most convenient means of transportation for men and materials, while of course the availability of water, cheap power and ready means of rapid communications are imperative. Once having chosen the future location for our installations, we must plan for the housing and the construction of the projected instruments, put them in operation and take care of their proper maintenance. These tasks must be carried out by men of multiple capabilities and training. In the following we shall enumerate some of the experts needed to insure the successful construction and operation of a telescope. And finally a competent group of astronomers, technicians, maintenance men and administrative staff is indispensable.

The Geologist

He must see to it that we do not build our telescope on sand. As far as I know this has never quite happened yet, but almost. In any event sliding earth formations—keeping in mind in particular long periods of heavy precipitation—earthquake faults, obliquely oriented strata of clay, lime and sandstone, decomposed granite, gneiss and the like must be avoided. In short, if there are any untrustworthy geological formations at the chosen site, the geologist must give us the details.

The Civil Engineer and the Contractor

Making use of the information obtained from the geologist, the contractor's first task is to reinforce the weak spots in the ground and test its load-carrying capacity, which must meet certain well-established standards. Loose debris and weak pockets must be cleaned out and filled properly to establish a stable base for the erection of the domes and the telescopes they are to house. This work, which so to speak is that of a dentist on a giant scale, necessitates the fortification of the ground with inserts of steel and concrete and is best done by a civil engineer with experience in the lateral bracing of power dams. An expert of this type is furthermore needed for the construction of the domes and for the mountings of the telescopes themselves.

The laboratories, dark rooms, storage rooms, offices, libraries, sanitary installations and first aid and maintenance facilities in many of the largest observatories of the world, as well as the living quarters for the observers, the roads of access and the means of transportation are so badly planned and so poorly kept up to date that the physical and the mental energy of the astronomers are often sadly taxed and partly wasted. Off and on I have been tempted to conclude that some of the engineer superintendents in charge, or the cognizant administrators, not only consider the astronomers as expendable but are bent on exterminating them. In any case, for the efficient operation of an observatory one might reasonably expect that observers who often work fifteen hours a day for a week in succession might be spared all bother with disagreeable and time-consuming daily chores. In many cases, especially at observatories whose directors are not capable or not willing to keep everybody strictly in line and who prefer to practice favoritism rather than justice, equal and considerate concern for all men on the staff as well as for the proper maintenance of all equipment has apparently been too much for which to hope.

The Mechanical Engineer

This expert must, before all, contribute his knowledge and experience towards the construction of small or large movable mountings of the telescopes, the precision drives and controls for the movements of the telescope itself, as well as those for the domes, elevators and necessary cranes. He must also be familiar with the construction and operation of all sorts of pumps, including the vacuum pumps which are necessary for the evacuation of the air from the giant containers being used for the aluminizing of large mirrors. Actually an electrical engineer is also needed, since the operation of one or more telescopes requires a great number of sophisticated electrical installations. It has been my experience that a rather surprising number of electrical engineers and technicians can also take care of all of the mechanical installations of an observatory, and vice versa.

Among the dozens of additional problems with which the engineers are faced, I mention as one of the most outstanding and difficult the cutting of small and large driving gears. Poor construction of these may cause catastrophic inefficiency in the operation of otherwise fine instruments. The completion of two of the largest and most modern telescopes in the world, for instance, was delayed for several years because of inexpert blundering in the construction of the necessary gears and bearings; the "takeover generation" had apparently thought it knew better and had not bothered to solicit the advice of those "old men" who had successfully designed and manufactured the large gear trains for the giant Palomar Hale Telescope.

Opticians, Instrument Makers, and Electronics Experts

Inasmuch as the mirrors and lenses for telescopes must be "figured," as we call it in the professional lingo, that is ground and polished to their exact shapes with a precision approaching a small fraction of a wavelength of light (that is to the order of one ten thousandth of a millimeter), we need a very expert optician to do the work. Likewise he must be able to adjust the optical lineups of the telescopes, spectrographs and all sorts of measuring instruments and cameras, possibly with the aid of one of the astronomers, although curiously enough there are few among the scientists who are capable of contributing much in this all-important art. This probably accounts for the fact that a majority of the telescopes in all observatories of the world suffers from chronic ill adjustment.

In addition to the optician we need an instrument maker who takes care of the construction of all mechanical apparatus that cannot be bought, that is special plateholders, focusing controls, testing and developing apparatus for photographic plates, so-called jiggle (schraffier) cameras, precision screws for measuring machines and comparators, blink apparatus and numerous devices that often must be made quickly.

And finally, photoelectric, electronic and photoelectronic recorders and instruments, as well as masers and lasers begin to play an ever more important role in astronomy, so that at least one more expert becomes indispensable. In fact, I do not know of any designer and builder of astronomical instruments who is equally and sufficiently capable in all the three fields of optical, mechanical, and electrical devices. But even a group of three competent experts in these three arts is not enough, since we are not only forced to buy ready-made instruments or parts of instruments on the market, but we must also "farm out" contracts for the design and the construction of many complex and entirely novel pieces of apparatus. I mention here only two among these devices whose immense potential value was not recognized by the professional astronomers for several decades. Either they did not have sufficient training as physicists and chemists, or they were too set in their ways of limited vision and did not want to listen. One of these devices is the objective transmission grating, so called because it must be of the same size as the whole opening or the full aperture of the telescope itself (or, in special cases equal to the cross section of the full beam of light within the instrument, wherever this beam has been made parallel). For a more detailed discussion of the potential power of objective transmission gratings I refer the reader to some of the existing literature, for instance, to my articles in the *Publications of the Astronomical Society of the Pacific*, 1941, Volume 53, page 242 and in *Die*

Sterne 1967, Volume 43, pages 89–92; See also F. Zwicky, *Morphology of Propulsive Power*, Monograph Number 1 of the Society for Morphological Research, Pasadena, California, 1962, page 162ff. and page 170ff.).

The second type of a most important device I wish to call attention to is the photoelectronic tubes and photoelectronic telescopes, which will be referred to in more detail on pp. 225–26.

The Aerodynamicist

This is one of the experts we shall be able to do without, once we are in a position to establish telescopes on the Moon or anywhere else in empty space. As long as we operate within the Earth's atmosphere, however, it would be a fatal mistake to ignore him and not solicit his advice. As an extreme case we should never forget the catastrophe that befell the Tacoma bridge over the Columbia River in 1940, which, through excitation by aerodynamic fluttering, developed such torsional vibrations that in the end it broke in two and fell completely apart. Neglect in planning for the effects of aerodynamic forces also resulted in serious limitations in the case of some of the radio telescopes, whose operation was in many ways impaired as a consequence. Likewise, for giant telescopes it is not only of the greatest importance to minimize aerodynamically induced oscillations through the proper construction of the domes, mountings, shutters and wind screens, which will absorb the shocks from gusts of wind and help dampen the effects from prolonged and accumulating forces due to atmospheric eddies, but great care must also be taken to prevent whirling dust and, in very bad weather, spray of fog being precipitated on any of the optically delicate surfaces of the mirrors and lenses or penetrating any of the sensitive parts of the driving mechanisms and control devices.

The Observer

The most perfect telescope is useless without a good observer. The ability for good and unbiased observing is in part inborn, but it may also be quite effectively acquired through proper education and persevering practice. Concerning this issue of education, it is a most amazing and almost unbelievable fact that it is essentially nonexistent as far as it concerns the use of telescopes. Indeed, how is an observer being acquainted with their operation? One of the "old men" or a night assistant hurriedly explains to the novice a few of the features of the telescope and shows him, equally hurriedly, how to operate it, and the education is already completed. Under these circumstances, with so many of the greenhorns left to themselves operating valuable equipment, it is rather astonishing that astronomy has fared so well as it actually has and that more fine instruments have not been hopelessly damaged or put out of action. In contrast, if we think of the intense training the members of the Olympic teams of the various nations have to go through, we begin to get some inkling of the unpardonable idiocy that characterizes the lack of education of the young observational astronomers as far as the operation and the most efficient use of modern and exceedingly costly telescopes is concerned.

But even with the availability of a good crew of observers, not all is said and done if we remember the thousands of excellent photographic plates and photoelectric recordings that are being filed away in convenient drawers, where they remain forgotten under the evermore accumulating layers of dust until they are rediscovered by later generations to reveal to them one of the common shortcomings of astronomers.

The Maintenance Personnel

For the efficiency of the operation of a telescope to be high, it must at all times be kept in good working order. This is not always easy since the astronomers themselves often cannot help too much. For instance, those of us who do our observing on Palomar Mountain actually live in Pasadena, 200 kilometers away. When we arrive on the mountain after a three-hour drive, eat lunch and check the instruments in the afternoon, some parts may be found to be out of order, and we often lose much time with small repairs, or we cannot correct or eliminate the defects at all, before starting the first night's work. This means essentially that for the smooth operation of all necessary equipment we must rely on our colleague who observed the night before to have reported any malfunctioning of the instruments or any damage done by him to the resident engineer superintendent. Failure to do so, or any disregard by the maintenance men of the instructions left by the departing observer can be very annoying and can in some cases have serious consequences. During my more than thirty years of work at the Palomar and Mount Wilson Observatories I have indeed witnessed a number of light to serious accidents, which happened because of insufficient communication and cooperation between the astronomers and the maintenance men or the superintendent on location. Night assistants present a particularly difficult problem; much could often be done, however, if some of the astronomers subscribed to the idea here advocated of direct cooperation between scientists and laymen, and if they actually inspired the night assistants to participate actively in their work, showing them how to contribute constructively to scientific research, naturally with promotion in position and proper remuneration for extra work. It seems that, long before my time, this type of approach was practiced by the founder of the Mount Wilson and Palomar Observatories, Dr. George Ellery Hale. For instance, my old friend and colleague Dr. M. L. Humason started on Mount Wilson as a handy man. He then served as night assistant and was finally given the position as a staff astronomer by Dr. Hale. In this capacity he proved to be one of the best observers of all times and was properly awarded an honorary Doctor's degree by Lund University in Sweden. Somewhat analogously, our night assistant at the 48-inch Schmidt Telescope on Palomar Mountain collaborated with me in the international supernova search and, in the period from January, 1960, to December, 1962, discovered five of these very rare objects. Unfortunately, the powers in being did not share my views and this cooperation came to an abrupt end by decree.

The Director and His Associates

Here we come to a particularly delicate issue. It would naturally be desirable to have a director of universal interests, who thoroughly understands the basic principles of theoretical and practical astronomy and astrophysics. He also should be an efficient administrator or be willing, if necessary, to delegate authority in this domain. Finally and before all he should not practice any favoritism and should know how to inspire all members of the observatory staff to ever greater achievements. Unfortunately the reality has mostly a different face. In my own experience I have met too many directors who, because of their ingrained scientific and human prejudices, invariably proceed to make decisions dictatorially. And in such cases they always choose members for their advisory observatory committees who are either harmless and inactive or who belong to that unfortunate class of ambitious climbers who cater to the aberrations of their superiors and in turn denounce all independent colleagues as nonconformists whose work need not be particularly supported. More often than not the shabbily treated heretics later prove actually to have been the ones who best knew where science was going and who in addition contributed most to human contacts and mutual understanding between scientists and laymen among all of the peoples of the world.

Things in the United States of America, for instance, went so far that pitifully unbalanced directors of observatories and other institutions appointed censuring committees, composed of pliable members of their staffs, which, in vicious league with similarly oriented editors and reviewing committees of leading scientific journals, flatly rejected important scientific manuscripts submitted by nonconformists, who thus were forced, after much loss of time, to send their findings to foreign journals. In one case of which I know, a censuring committee of this type could be forced to abdicate and dissolve only after a long and bitter controversy, and after it could be shown that the director of the institution had acted illegally and in violation of the well-known code of conduct entitled *The Rights and Responsibilities of Universities and Their Faculties* (a statement by the association of American universities, adopted Tuesday, March 24, 1953). I recommend that readers who are interested in these issues acquaint themselves with this excellently written document. In any event one should expect the directors of all observatories to encourage all of the scientists and engineers on the staff to present their results to the scientific world without interference by them or men appointed by them.

In view of the immense flood of nonsense being published by local newspapers, national magazines and the like, another useful project for the directors and the staffs of scientific institutions looms on the horizon. If indeed the public is to be informed authoritatively about scientific activities and new results gained, we must see to it that the investigators in question be given the opportunity to do more and more of the reporting themselves, as it is being done in many of the leading newspapers and various popular magazines in Europe. Information transmitted second hand to the general public, especially after it has been dramatized by journalists looking for "scoops" or by incompetent so-called researchers of some of the magazines with large circulation, can only be a pitiful substitute for scientists addressing the man in the street directly.

In conclusion it may be suggested that it would be of considerable importance to carry out a morphological study of those principles that will eventually allow us to choose the best qualified men as directors of observatories or, for that matter, as directors or presidents of any other scientific or technical institution. We might find, of course, that a directorship should not be a permanent position and that changes should be made more or less frequently. Furthermore it might be an advantage to elect the men in charge by popular vote of the members of the respective staffs. As to the constitution of observatory committees and other similar governing bodies, they should certainly never be allowed to assume hierarchical stature, a state of affairs which, in the United States, is clearly not permissible if I correctly interpret the code of conduct accepted in *The Rights and Responsibilities of Universities and Their Faculties*, which I cited above.

The lucky fact that off and on an ideal director appears on the scene out of the blue sky, as was the case with Dr. George

Ellery Hale, can not alter our conviction that a systematic morphological approach is imperative if we are to make sure that dictatorial aberrations of the minds of future directors of observatories will not further impede the progress of astronomy and the application of the results gained for the enrichment of all human activities. In the meantime it will be well to keep in mind that even very good (notice, I do not say very great) scientists may, humanly speaking, leave much to be desired, as was the case with Tycho Brahe (1546–1601), who treated his assistant Johannes Kepler (1571–1630) most miserably.

Outlook

From what we have said in the preceding it has become clear that in the field of astronomy much remains to be done by the unbiased morphologist. Perhaps we need not fear that Giordano Bruno (1548–1600), if he came back today, would be burned at the stake because of his promotion of some advanced ideas and concepts. I am less certain, however, that a future Galileo Galilei (1564–1642) would not be denounced by some of those present-day astronomers who have had themselves promoted to hierarchical positions of power, but who have never understood what independence really means, not to mention having lived it. And it is still possible that important developments will be stopped for years and even for decades by pathological and self-centered individuals who occupy positions of power. The difficulties which the idea of radio-astronomy encountered should serve as an example. In 1931, K. G. Janski (1905–50), in the course of his work at the research laboratories of the Bell Telephone Company, discovered the influx of radio waves coming from outer space and, with particularly high intensity, from certain regions of the Milky Way. Together with two of my colleagues at the California Institute of Technology in Pasadena, Professor G. Potapenko (1894–   ) and Russell W. Porter (1872–1949) we proposed to start checking up on Janski's results immediately. Porter made one of his now famous types of drawings (production illustration drawing) of the antenna which we proposed to use. This drawing remains preserved in the archives of our institute; but we were not granted at that time the two hundred dollars for which we applied because the cognizant professional astronomers claimed that there could not exist any cosmic radio waves at the intensity announced by Janski. Even the more decisive observations by G. Reber (1911–) a decade later made no impression, until the Australian investigators J. G. Bolton (1922–) and G. Stanley (1921–) decisively proved the existence of the new type of extraterrestrial radio radiation and at the same time localized specific objects which emit them, one of them being the Crab Nebula (Messier 1), which is thought to be the remnant of the Chinese supernova of the year 1054 A.D.

Similar delays occurred with the introduction of the photoelectronic telescope (see the author's Halley Lecture, delivered at Oxford on May 12, 1948, and reprinted in *The Observatory*, 1948, Volume 68, pages 121–143), with rocket borne instruments and space research in general, as well as with the construction of large objective transmission gratings already mentioned.

On the other hand I wish to caution all hotheads that it is not advisable to try to do everything at the same time, a mistake which is often committed by individuals and by institutions whose funds are limited. For instance, the construction of multipurpose telescopes is in general not to be recommended. It is better to concentrate one's attention on specific problems and to build instruments best adapted for their solution. Actually one often discovers subsequently that such instruments can also be used effectively for other and not originally apparent purposes. As an example I mention the 18-inch Schmidt telescope on Palomar Mountain, whose construction I promoted in 1935 for the specific task of supernovae, which I suspected to be the most giant eruptions of energy in the universe that could actually be discovered and observed in action from their start. I put this instrument into operation on the night of September 5, 1936, and immediately started a systematic survey of several thousand galaxies. This proved to be a most rewarding project, inasmuch as twenty of the very elusive supernovae were discovered by my assistant J. J.

Johnson and myself in the period from 1936 until 1941. As gratuities, so to speak, the following discoveries were made in addition with the 18-inch Schmidt telescope: (a) The first dwarf and pygmy galaxies were found, (b) luminous intergalactic formations were discovered whose existence had previously been vehemently denied, (c) the blue Humason-Zwicky (HZ) stars were discovered, which represent a new important class of objects in the general directions of the two galactic poles of the Milky Way, and (d) many new clusters of galaxies, variable stars, common novae, and flare stars were found. At the same time much of the observational material was gathered for the preparation of our six-volume catalogue of about fifty thousand of the brightest galaxies in the northern half of the celestial sphere and of ten thousand clusters of galaxies seen in the same area. For the construction of the 18-inch Schmidt telescope, its housing, a full-size objective prism, a small remuneration for my assistant, and the operational costs for the whole project during ten years, only about fifty thousand dollars were expended. This probably represents the highest efficiency, as measured in results achieved per dollar invested, of any telescope presently in use (and perhaps of any ever built, with the exception of Galilei's little refractor).

In conclusion, a few suggestions may be summarized as they refer to the construction of future telescopes. Some of the most important ones, I think, are as follows:

(a) Groups of expert collaborators should be formed who will occupy themselves with reviews and analyses of the basic problems most likely to be solved through future research in astronomy. For instance, from objects located beyond the boundaries of the solar system we can gather information only through the recording of the incoming light rays, and generally of electromagnetic radiations of all wave lengths, as well as of cosmic rays and possibly of atomic rays and neutrinos. (Recorders for gravitational waves of possible gravitons have not as yet been invented.) Our efforts must therefore be concentrated on morphological reviews of the possible *interrelations among all physical phenomena* that are associated with the various radiations mentioned and of the observational means which will enable us to record and analyze them. The information thus accumulated should be summarized periodically in concise monographs and made available to all workers in the field.

(b) *Courses on integral engineering* should be conducted at some universities and technical schools in order to impress future astronomers and builders of observatories with the necessity of visualizing large complexes of interrelated phenomena, which necessity must be understood if science is to contribute materially towards the integration of a true world image.

(c) And finally within industrial concerns somewhat more specialized groups of experts should be formed, who jointly dispose of all of the essential knowledge and capabilities delineated in the preceeding paragraphs and who are capable of constructing any desired type of telescope under contractual guarantee of optimum performance and minimum cost.

What has been said about telescopes and observatories applies in principle not only to any other set of scientific instruments and any other scientific laboratories, but also to the construction of all types of machines and vehicles, as well as to a multitude of commercial enterprises. I repeat that in all of these cases it will be wise to start with an enumeration and evaluation of all, and even of the apparently smallest factors, which might have to be considered for practical inclusion. To this theme, a few more words:

SOME REMARKS ABOUT A FURTHER SUBJECT: THE AUTOMOBILE

In order to familiarize the readers further with the idea of integral engineering, we will discuss some of the annoying types of defects in automobiles. For instance, my wife and I just bought a new car and discovered too late that the lock for the ignition key is located on the left side of the steering column and, to make it worse, so close to it that we are forced to manipulate the key awkwardly with our left hands and therefore find it difficult to introduce it properly into the key hole without galling the smooth metal surfaces or ruining them entirely. The body of the same car, a station wagon, is shaped so unfortunately that, on driving, a beautiful Kármán vortex street is generated at just the right height trailing the car so that in bad weather the rear window is effectively being splashed with charges of mud, while in dry weather it will be peppered with road oil, dust, sand, and small pebbles. As a consequence the view of the driver towards the rear is badly obstructed after a few minutes of driving. In another car the clutch pedal and the emergency brake had to be operated with the left foot. The brake could not be released gradually but only abruptly, by kicking up a small lever with the left hand. This arrangement leads to very dangerous situations whenever quick action is imperative. In particular it may prove quite impossible to start on a hill whenever one is stalled. One then has to resort to rolling backwards downhill, which can be perilous if the road is narrow, steep, and winding, especially if another vehicle is coming up the hill.

I also remember a car with which I started from Pasadena on a warm winter's day and arrived at the Palomar Mountain Observatory at an altitude of 1,800 meters in a snowstorm with the temperature at minus 10 degrees Centigrade. Since I had no antifreeze in the radiator I decided to drain it. After some search I discovered that this could be done only by opening two spigots so poorly located that I skinned my hand bloody to open the first, while I could not reach the second at all. To do that I had to run to our machine shop and get a long iron rod with proper attachment.

And still another case: An American agency once held a new car ready for me in Antwerp, from where I drove it to Switzerland. Over every little hill along the way, and especially later on in the Alps, it overheated so badly that I had to carry water cans with me, stop every ten minutes and cool and refill the radiator. Returning with this "lemon" to New York, the first gas station attendant I consulted after disembarking laughed in my face because I had not yet heard that the factory had made a slight mistake and had recalled 600,000 radiators to replace them with larger ones.

Summa summarum I am inclined to claim that there has never actually been a stock car run off the assembly line free of all these ludicrous defects, which certainly should be avoidable after the production of several hundred million automobiles during the past few decades. And who is to be blamed? The following episode perhaps sheds some light on this question.

A few years ago I was invited by the director of the research laboratories of the Ford Motor Company in Detroit to deliver a lecture on morphological research. On that occasion I asked why automobile engines with greater efficiency and cars with better over-all body construction had not been built. In a more or less casual way I had previously requested topological performance charts from directors and engineers of various motor companies. I had found that they were not available anywhere. From such charts, if correctly calculated, one should be able to read of the distances that cars of a given weight can be driven over a smooth and level concrete highway, at some constant speed in kilometers (or miles) per hour with say one liter (or one gallon) of a certain type of gasoline. In other words I was looking for information on the so-called over-all thermopropulsive efficiency of a motor car, which depends, in the first place, on the thermodynamic efficiency of the motor (reciprocating engine, gas turbine, Diesel engine, etc.) and involves a comprehensive analysis of the energies lost per second (power loss) as frictional heat, vibrational heat, rolling friction of the wheels and work of mechanical abrasion as well as aerodynamic resistance. Although topological performance charts for rockets, aerial propulsive power plants and airplanes have been constructed and constantly improved for many years, analogous diagrams, charts, and tables for automobiles did not exist when I asked for them, and I should not be surprised to learn that even today none of them can be found. In any case, no one has as yet publicized his knowledge of how far a car of given weight can be driven over a smooth level road at any given speed with a given quantity of various fuels, if all losses are minimized as far as this is possible with present day construction methods and use of materials as they are actually available.

To return to the resident engineers of the Research Laboratories of the Ford Motor Company, they invited me to come to a certain window where they could point to another building located within the complex of the factory. In partial answer to my inquiry they informed me that up to 200 million dollars a year were spent in this other building in order to plan and construct new body designs for the company's automobiles. They complained that as a result of these fashioning activities all sorts of atrocities, such as giant rear fins, fancy hoods, and chrome-plated decor, etc., were being produced to impress the customers, and among them especially the ladies, that the last *cri de Paris* has arrived and the last years' models are now completely antiquated compared with the new ones. Subsequently these esthetic and mechanical monstrosities are being presented to the engineers for incorporation of their more or less unimportant items, like motors, transmissions, steering and braking mechanisms, and so on. Under these circumstances it is not surprising that harried engineers show little enthusiasm for fundamental morphological research on the possible optimum propulsive power efficiencies of automobiles and the maximum safety that might be achieved if all the shortcomings of drivers and all the malices of streets and highways, of weather and of traffic were taken into account. And this is not to mention making any concerted efforts to suppress the noxious components in the exhaust gases, which today are one of the major causes of the devastating smog in and around Los Angeles and other highly populated and motorized centers of the world.

The few examples discussed in the preceding should suffice to show that for all large-scale projects—such as those handled by the automobile industry, by national road-building programs, railroad systems, airlines, and so on—the cooperation of competent groups of experts, who are at the same time professional morphologists and thus capable of *integral planning* and *integral engineering*, has become an absolute necessity in today's world.

Third Appliction of the Method of Field Coverage:
Interrelations of Ideas and Concepts

THE MORPHOLOGICAL ANALYSIS OF SOME CULTURAL AND ECONOMIC ASPECTS OF THE PRODUCTION OF POSTAGE STAMPS

Once one is accustomed to thinking in terms of vast complexes of interrelations between objects, phenomena, and concepts, he will automatically be inspired by new and surprising ideas and will find it easy to make discoveries and inventions that not only escaped all the more conventional minds but may even have been missed by imaginative professionals and experts in the respective fields. In illustration of this claim I refer again to one of my personal experiences.

One of my old friends, who had lost everything because of the expropriation of all property held by foreigners in one of the countries that emerged after World War II, returned to Switzerland practically penniless. All that he had been able to save was a few hundred postage stamps, for which the regular stamp dealers did not offer him any acceptable price. In order not to offend him with the presentation of some alms, I offered to buy his stamps. Since I am not a collector, I passed them on to my little daughters with the advice that they study them as a vast source of information on various subjects, such as art, history, linguistics, geography, psychology, and so on.

It thus occurred to me that postage stamps really are of far greater potential value than merely as objects of financial interest to merchants or psychological palliatives to millions of collectors. From long experience I knew that, on systematic application of the method of field coverage to all aspects of the production and distribution of stamps, I would come up with some new and startling discoveries. In retrospect I think I am justified in claiming, for instance, that it never occurred to any of the millions of collectors all over the world to investigate why certain personalities are being depicted on postage stamps and, what is far more remarkable, why certain others are not. I also suspect that no historian ever asked himself this question, which actually is a most profound one.

Indeed, pursuing the above suggested line of thought, I found, for example, that no picture of a real person has ever appeared on any of the regular Swiss postage stamps, which only show representations of certain symbolic personalities, like William Tell and his boy, from whose head he shot the apple, and of course Helvetia. (Only on the semiregular postage stamps—which are issued for the benefit of Pro Juventute, Pro Patria, and other philanthropic organizations—are well-known writers, educators, artists, scientists, statesmen, and military leaders being honoured.) Since Switzerland endeavours to act (or to appear to act) as a democracy should, we can easily understand its reluctance to allow portraits of actual persons on its postage stamps. This determination to steer clear of any and all favoritism is in clear contrast to the habits of the so-called peoples' democracies, which exhibit their dictators on postage stamps, posters, and monuments whenever and wherever they can.

On the other hand, it is at first sight a complete mystery why none of the last three German emperors ever appeared on any of the postage stamps of the Reich. Furthermore, none of the stamps issued by United Germany in the course of the fifty years after the Franco-Prussian War of 1870–71 made use of any portraits of either living or past men or women, althought this is not too surprising, since the emperors were not depicted. (Bavaria, which had its own postage stamps until 1920, however was an exception.) Only in 1923 did Germany abandon its tradition of "impersonal" postage stamps through an issue in honour of Heinrich von Stephan, one of the cofounders of the International Postal Union, which at that time celebrated its semicentennial.

The emperors William I and Frederic III cannot be found on any of the German stamps, and the certainly not very modest William II only once, as far as I know, on a stamp issued in celebration of the unification of Germany. On this issue he does not appear by himself, however, but surrounded by a group of high dignitaries. Like Helvetia on the Swiss stamps, only symbolic figures like Germania appear on the German stamps issued in the period from 1871 to 1923. But this use of symbols and the complete neglect of the three emperors must certainly have some justification entirely different from the one that accounts for the absence on the Swiss stamps of portraits and figures of actual men and women. I am inclined to suspect that Count Otto von Bismarck, the German Chancellor under William I, is responsible for the "impersonal" stamps of Imperial Germany. In his persistent endeavours to achieve the unification of the German Reich, Bismarck used methods and procedures that must be characterized as ruthless. In the end, nevertheless, he was a great statesman. It seems that even the most trifling circumstance did not escape his attention if it had any possible significance for the unification of the German states and, I think, for the preservation of the peace of the world. After his Prussian armies, under the brilliant leadership of General von Moltke at Koeniggraetz, had beaten the armies of the Austrian empire, which stood against the unification of Germany, he let it go at that and did not ask for the secession of enemy territory or any compensation. Likewise, after his victory over Napoleon III, he would have been satisfied with an indemnity of five billion gold francs and did not want to annex Alsace-Lorraine. On this issue he was unfortunately overruled by the emperor, who followed the advice of his top generals. What interests us here, however, is the fact that Bismarck was perpetually forced to treat the kings of Bavaria and Swabia (Württemberg), as well as the Grand Duke of Badensia, with the greatest of care and consideration in order to keep them securely on his side and prevent the secession of their states from the Reich. For these reasons even the slightest provocation of the said gentlemen had to be meticulously avoided. I suspect that, in Bismarck's judgement, such provocation might have resulted if he had allowed the picture of William I, formerly only the King of Prussia but now the Emperor of Germany, to be printed on billions of postage stamps and distributed all over the country and the world.

On the other hand, Queen Victoria and all of the kings and queens after her are not to be missed on any of the postage stamps of Great Britain. The same is true of all the members of the Commonwealth, for India, and all the issues for the numerous colonies, settlements, and the like, as long as they were subjects of the British Crown. This in fact was one of the more minor aspects of that unfortunate type of colonialism, which in large measure is responsible for many of the bitter conflicts ravaging the world today.

The above brief field coverage of some of the political, historical, cultural, and psychological aspects of the production and the use of postage stamps can be extended in a great many directions. Some of the readers may be interested in the propagandistic or the artistic uses of postage stamps. It is highly regrettable that many of the new states indulge in disgusting glorifications of revolutions and war. Fortunately, however, some other countries prefer to honour great humanitarians, artists, and men of science on their postage stamps, which are often superbly designed.

In conclusion, attention must be called to the possibility of following the development of living standards, inflation, and other aspects of economic life through a study of the postal tariffs, which can be read on the stamps of various countries. The lowest and highest denominations used at any given time may indeed be taken as measures either of the stability or the more or less rapid devaluation of the currencies of these countries. Gradual changes of the postage rates will be found in periods when commodity price indices change slowly. On the other hand, catastrophic events, military defeats, revolutions, ascendancies of incapable dictatorships, and economic instabilities of all sorts will be reflected in marked changes of the postal rates. Some of my readers may be interested in pursuing this subject further and studying stamps and coins from this point of view. Even some schools of law and of international business economics might profitably conduct courses on the comparative financial stability of different nations as it can be deduced from a study of postage stamps and coins, as well as from the relative circulation of silver,

Table I: Development of Swiss Postal Tariffs for Domestic Mail*

All values in centimes　　　　　*4.3 centimes = 1 U.S. cent*

VALID FROM:	1.V 1900	1.I 1906	1.II 1911	1.I 1915	1.I 1918	1.IX 1918	1.I 1921	1.VII 1925	1.I 1927	1.I 1928	1.IV 1935	1.I 1935	1.IX 1937	1.VII 1939	1.X 1940	1.III 1941	1.XI 1947	1.I 1947	1.I 1948	1.III 48
LETTERS UP TO 250 GRAMS:																				
Local	5				10	10														10
General	10			15	15		20													20
PACKAGES 250 TO 100 GRAMS:																				
Local								30	30					20				20		30
General																30				30
SIMPLE POSTCARDS	5			7.5	7.5		10											10		10
ANSWER NOT PAID FOR	10			15	15		10											10		10
ANSWER PAID FOR	10						20													20

* unchanged from 1948 until 1966

gold and paper currency. It is obvious that innumerable themes for theses for the Bachelor, Master, and Doctor's degrees can be found within the vast complexes of the interrelations of the various aspects involved in the production and use of postage stamps. Reviews of the type shown in Tables I and II, as they represent developments in Switzerland should also be compiled for other countries. These tables, which were kindly put at my disposal by the central office of the Swiss Postal Administration (PTT) in Berne, list the postal tariffs for letters, packages and postcards for domestic communication from 1900 until 1966, as well as the tariffs for letters, postcards, and registered mail to foreign countries from 1854 until 1966.

Table I shows that the postal tariffs in Switzerland were increased extraordinarily slowly. They have only been about doubled in the course of the past sixty-six years. The cost of living index in the same period increased manyfold. The postage of twenty centimes or 4.65 American cents for domestic letters (and of 10 centimes or 2.3 cents for local letters) is even lower than in the United States of America, although the mail is distributed twice a day and in the United States only once a day. Of course, the mail in America has to travel much further on the average, although not on such tortuous paths. Also, in Switzerland the mail carrier cannot just drop the mail into any conveniently located boxes along the route, but must deliver it even at some of the most outrageously isolated locations in the Alps.

From Table II we learn that there was no uniform tariff for mail from Switzerland to foreign countries before the founding of the International Postal Union in 1875. Later on this confusion was gradually eliminated until from 1892 on, the charges for letters, postcards and registered mail to all countries not only became the same but, in some cases, were considerably lower than they had been before 1875. This, of course, was in part the result of improved means of transportation, the railroads in particular. Analogous developments occurred later with respect to the charges for airmail, which were lowered several times, whenever the technical improvements in air transport justified it.

Table II: Swiss Postal Tariffs for Foreign Mail

Dates	Letter under 15 grams	Postcards	Registration Fee
15. XII. 1854 France	15, 20, or 35 centimes	Not accepted	Double of the postage
1. VI. 1869			
Germany	50		25
France	30		40
Italy	30		30
Austria	25		25
U.S.A.	80		50
1. VII. 1876			
World Postal Union	25	10	10
Other Countries		Depending on distance	
1. IV. 1879			
World Postal Union			
Tariff I	25	10	25
Tariff II	40	10	25
Other Countries		Depending on distance	
30. VIII. 1884			
World Postal Union	25	10	25
Other Countries	75	Not accepted	50
1. VII. 1892	25	10	25
1. II. 1921	40	25	40
15. V. 1924	40	20	40
1. X. 1924	30	20	40
1. VII. 1930	30	20	30
1. III. 1948	40	25	40
1. IV. 1959 (unchanged until 1966)	50	30	50

As an astronomer I am particularly interested in the appearance of astronomical themes on the faces of postage stamps. Fortunately I did not have to peruse all of the issues of the world since A. P. Mayernik, unknown to me, compiled a comprehensive article on "Astronomical Postage Stamps" and published it in the well known American journal *Sky and Telescope*. (Individual reprints of this article are obtainable from the office of Sky Publications, Harvard Observatory, Cambridge, Massachusetts 02138, U.S.A., for fifty cents a copy.)

Obviously, today, because of the tremendous number of postage stamps being issued by so many countries, we may find depicted on them almost any subject we might wish to name—from space travel to all sorts of sports and Olympic games, as well as plants, trees, flowers, animals and so on. As a consequence we now have collectors of motifs. These people, and in fact stamp collectors in general, might well avail themselves of the morphological method of complete field coverage, which would help them derive the greatest benefits from their hobby.

4

The Morphological Methods II:
The Method of the
Morphological Box

We repeat here once more some of the essential aspects of the Morphological Approach.

(a) Morphological research is *totality research,* which in a completely unbiased way attempts to derive all the solutions of any given problem.

(b) The morphological approach has developed its own characteristic procedures, such as the method of the morphological box which will be explained and applied in this chapter.

(c) The morphological approach gives us the maximum guarantee that no circumstance is overlooked that might be of importance for the satisfactory accomplishment of any task before us.

(d) Morphological thinking helps to clarify all issues and conflicts that might arise among men, and it serves to establish the best means of communication among them as well as to avoid misunderstanding.

(e) Since the morphological approach leads to all-embracing vistas and perspectives and also strives for perfect achievements, it is logically, artistically, and ethically extraordinarily satisfying. The total solution of any problem, derived with the aid of morphological methods, affords the same pleasure and deep contentment as the successful first ascent of a difficult mountain peak.

Both achievements are technically and artistically complete in themselves. They are unassailable and nobody can really take them away from us.

(f) Those who have successfully made use of the morphological approach are confident that there are hardly any problems they might attempt to solve without any hope of success. As a result of this conviction many tasks that seemed impossibly difficult immediately assume a less forbidding appearance. This must not, however, be interpreted to mean that morphological research can be pursued effectively without any previous solid knowledge and sound experience.

(g) Morphological research is a rich source of inspiration for the continued enrichment of life, because it is not only technically fruitful, but its pursuit is also very pleasurable, inasmuch as one's intuition is constantly being stimulated, and new surprising and constructive ideas in all fields of human endeavour are continually forthcoming.

(h) The morphological approach enables us to systematize our inventiveness. It allows us to make discoveries and inventions methodically, and in some cases almost automatically. Without that, we are forced to resort to haphazard procedures of trial and error.

(i) Expressing it pointedly, we may say that the *morphologist is a professional genius.* In other words, it is his profession to be a genius who is capable of pursuing original research and making discoveries and inventions in all fields of human endeavour. Those who are commonly thought to be geniuses are actually amateurs whose accomplishments in restricted fields are more or less accidental and bear the mark of dilettantism.

(j) Morphologists are convinced that *every individual is a potential genius. That is, every man, woman, and child is in some very particular sense unique, irreplaceable and incomparable.* I intend to make a concerted attempt at explaining and justifying these claims in a forthcoming book entitled *Everyone a Genius,* in which I shall try to show how important it would be for our whole system of education, and thus for the future of the human community and the world, if this simple fact were generally recognized and properly appreciated. It will therefore be up to the morphologists to make people really believe in themselves and to conceive of tests and criteria which will help them, each to recognize his own very particular genius and shape his life accordingly. What every man needs in order to achieve emotional stability is the certain knowledge of his unique individual capabilities on the one hand, and the assurance that he may expect all of those who have also overcome their aberrations to recognize his inherent capabilities and pool their efforts with his own for the purpose of constructing a sound world. In order to achieve a harmonious and stabilized human society, it is therefore of imperative importance that everyone recognize his true potentialities and be given the chance to develop them freely and fully.

Among the many methods and procedures that have been conceived and perfected through the morphological approach, the *construction of the morphological box* of all possible aspects and solutions of any given problem, as well as the unbiased evaluation of the solutions found, is one of the most effective. This method enables us to make discoveries and inventions in a systematic way, and it is a sure guide in the exploration of the basic interrelations among all conceivable families of objects and of the physical, chemical, and biological phenomena that govern their actions and interactions. With the aid of this method we also can gain deep insights into the inner worlds of men, that is their visions, ideas, concepts, emotions, and motivations. For the construction of any morphological box and for the subsequent evaluation of the information that may be contained in it we proceed as follows:

First Step. The problem to be solved must be very concisely formulated.

Second Step. All of the parameters that might be of importance for the solution of the given problem must be localized and analyzed.

Third Step. The morphological box or multidimensional matrix, which contains all of the potential solutions of the given problem, is constructed.

Fourth Step. All the solutions contained in the morphological box are closely scrutinized and evaluated with respect to the purposes that are to be achieved.

Fifth Step. The optimally suitable solutions are being selected and are practically applied, provided the necessary means are available. This reduction to practice requires in general a supplemental morphological study.

In the following we shall present three applications of the method of the morphological box, which deal respectively with the totality of certain groups of *physical objects*, the totality of of selected *physical phenomena*, and the totality of a few important complexes of *ideas and concepts*. We shall furthermore describe a few of the large-scale problems that have been studied with the aid of the method of the morphological box, as well as some that are in the process of being analyzed now. Success was actually achieved in many cases only because of the meticulous manner with which the five steps of procedure enumerated above were executed. In many of the conventional projects of the past, which were carried out without the benefit of the morphological approach, neglect of the exact formulation of the task at hand and the goals to be achieved often led to misunderstandings and catastrophic failures. It is therefore important to use exact definitions and to work with unambiguous rules and directives, as we shall briefly elaborate.

The Importance of Exact Definitions

As a first example we mention the strenuous efforts Professor J. B. Rhine of Duke University in Durham, North Carolina, has made to prove the existence of extrasensory perception (ESP). Rhine thought to have found persons who, when locked up in a completely closed room, were able to visualize the arrangements of playing cards that had been laid out by others in adjacent rooms. This has led to interminable discussions among mathematicians and psychologists as to whether the results obtained could be explained on the basis of mathematical probability theory or whether the media in question were endowed with extrasensory perception. To many of those who participated in these controversies it must have become clear that the exchanges of arguments could be prolonged ad infinitum if a sounder basis for the tests were not established. The fatal mistake of those who conducted the experiments on extrasensory perception and who believed in its reality was that they had really not strictly defined their problem and they had actually never conceived of any tests that were unambiguous and incontestable. Indeed, there is nothing extrasensory about any arrangements of cards in the first place. And in the second place information about these arrangements can again be transmitted through the use of physical (that is sensory) phenomena in many ways. For the tests to be significant one of two conditions, or preferably both, must be satisfied.

First there must exist no possibility whatever to transmit by physical phenomena any knowledge about the test object to the person who is supposed to be endowed with extrasensory perception. And second it would be desirable if the test object were itself abstract in character and not at all an actual body or physical phenomenon. With these conditions in mind the following two tests would appear suitable.

Assuming that no physical phenomenon whatever is transmitted with a velocity faster than light in vacuum, it would amount to extrasensory perception if anybody could predict the appearance of the many future supernovae and the characteristics of the galaxies in which they will be discovered, say exactly ten years before their flareups become actually observable with the telescopes on Earth. If Professor Rhine or anybody else will produce the prophet who without fail will thus be able to preannounce the appearance of supernovae in various galaxies I shall be prepared to listen and devote adequate time and effort to investigating the respective claims. I have spent a good part of my life in the search for supernovae, and I have discovered forty-five of them. With present day large Schmidt telescopes equipped with proper full-size transmission gratings, or with a photoelectronic telescope and computer, a single observer might conceivably find a few hundred supernovae a year. Any person who can do better with his extrasensory pickup will therefore certainly have to be heard.

I should take it as still another indication for extrasensory perception if anybody, barring the inventor or discoverer himself, could predict the exact day on which a certain investigator, who is to be named, will solve one of the famous problems of science and technology that has been bothering us for so long, for instance the great Fermat problem in number theory. This problem concerns a theorem which was stated by the great French mathematician Pierre de Fermat (1601–65) but which no one has as yet been able to solve. Likewise, any prediction as to when and where and by whom the so-called three-body problem in celestial mechanics will be solved, or a cure for cancer will be found, might provide an acceptable proof for the reality of extrasensory perception.

I repeat that no statement about extrasensory perception can be taken seriously unless those who make it have conducted tests that strictly conform to the true and uncompromising meaning of the concept of a nonphysical transmission of information.

Another example, where a deeper understanding of the subject matter at hand can only be gained if all concepts are strictly defined, is the following: The discussion about the totality of all possible energy transformations, which I shall present later, assumes a deeper meaning only if the *concept of energy* is formulated as concisely as possible. In any case energy must be defined clearly enough to enable every experimental physicist and chemist to recognize it in its various forms and to measure it whenever he wishes to do so. It is a rather remarkable fact that, although all competent experimental scientists and engineers experience no difficulty in identifying energy in its various aspects and disguises, very few among the thousands of texts on physics, chemistry and mechanics in circulation give an adequate definition of this most important concept. And some of them are downright defeatist. For instance, in that interesting and most modern compendium entitled *The Feynman Lectures on Physics* (Addison-Wesley Publishing Company, Inc., Redding, Massachusetts, 1963–1965), which was written by my three colleagues at the California Institute of Technology, Professors R. P. Feynman, R. B. Leighton and M. Sands, we read, "It is of importance to realize that in physics today we have no knowledge of what energy *is.*" This in my opinion goes too far and is a totally useless statement. Indeed, strictly speaking, it is of no interest to physicists to know what energy *is*, quite apart from the fact that it is philosophically a meaningless question. What we *must* know, however, is *first*, how to recognize the appearance of energy as well as how to associate it with certain evident phenomena and, *secondly*, how we can measure it. To both of these questions, of course, physicists have positive and very definite answers, and that is all that is needed in science. For all practical and theoretical purposes it is sufficient to define energy *as that attribute of matter and radiation that can always be transformed totally or in part into kinetic energy of a given material body*. If such a body is first at rest with respect to an observer, and this body is subsequently set in motion, we say that it has gained kinetic energy as seen from this observer and that this energy was transmitted to the body from some phenomenological content or attribute of another body or from radiation space. Such contents, which can produce kinetic energy of a standard body, we also designate as energies, and we have learned so far that such energies can appear in ten different disguises, which we will discuss later. The phenomena with which these various types of energy may appear to be associated are known as electricity, magnetism, heat, gravitation, chemical and nuclear reactions and so on. Our strict and practically most useful definition therefore states that every form of energy is capable of being transformed so as to put any material body in motion with respect to an observer or a system of coordinates relative to which it was originally at rest.

Some Attributes That Distinguish Man From Animal

In connection with the preceding discussion concerning the necessity of exact definitions in all fields of research and communication we must not fail to emphasize that it is precisely this faculty that secures for man his very unique position and power among all living beings. Only man is capable of objectively formulating concepts and problems that involve abstractions from the real world and which he can transmit from one generation to the next and thus accumulate knowledge as time passes.

As an example, I mention one of the most important abstractions we derive from the physical world, namely *the mathematical point*. For purposes of definition we consider two identical real bodies, for instance two equally flat circular disks cut out of cardboard. These disks can be placed on a table so as to be clearly separated, or they can cover each other partly, and finally they may be superimposed exactly so as to appear as a single disk. We now arrive at the idea of a mathematical point by imagining that the two disks shrink continually until their diameters become immeasurably small. At that stage we cannot any more talk of the disks as being partly coincident and partly separated. There remain only the two cases of their being clearly separated or exactly covering each other (the physicists say that the two points in this case are coincident). Since a partial coverage and a simultaneous partial separation for our two limiting bodies of infinitely small size is not any more possible, we call these objects mathematical points. As I have shown in my book, *Morphological Astronomy* (Springer Verlag, Berlin, 1957), the fact that we generally consider the space in which we live as three-dimensional and continuous has its origin in our capability to conceive of these abstract limiting bodies, the mathematical points. We repeat that in contradistinction to real material objects—which can be either clearly separated, strictly coincident or partly separated and partly overlapping—two mathematical points can only be separated or coincident: A third alternative does not exist.

Since for animals abstract concepts of this character, as well as the accumulation of knowledge through objective records such as books and the communication of the respective information to other animals, do not exist, we conclude that only man can communicate with others within a three-dimensional space in order to transmit purely spatial information. This means that animals, say birds, must transmit to each other more than three data (coordinates, or values of certain suitable parameters) if they attempt to agree on meeting at a certain location within the Earth's atmosphere. These considerations provide typical illustrations of the fact that the unrelenting pursuit and application of the morphological approach not only aids us in the solving of given problems, but it invariably opens unexpected vistas and leads to new queries, the answers to which must often be sought through entirely new methods and procedures.

In the above mentioned case, animals of necessity operating in a multidimensional space, we must first make tests to prove that they do not succeed to meet at a given place if they do not transmit to each other more than three simple data. It is most likely that their space of operation is at least nine dimensional (see F. Zwicky, *Morphological Astronomy*, Springer, Berlin, 1957).

Leaving these abstract considerations aside, we turn to a more prosaic application of the method of the morphological box, which nevertheless drastically illustrates its power and efficiency in successfully carrying out many large-scale practical operations.

First Application of the Method of the Morphological Box: A Totality of Interrelations Between Objects; Aid to War-Stricken Scientific Libraries

At the beginning of World War II it occurred to me, without any doubt whatsoever, that much would be destroyed during the course of the war in the way of material and spiritual values. If the world were to survive reasonably after the war, provisions would have to be made to restore or reconstruct these values. But speed of reconstruction after the war would depend on long-range and early planning. Most of my colleagues of good will, however, were busily occupied winning the war, and they were mostly absent from their homes in Pasadena and scattered all over the United States and the world. I could not therefore count on much collaboration from my scientific friends. Since I was myself heavily engaged in helping to bring Hitler, Mussolini, and Hirohito to their knees, I could not hope to deal with the problem of the most important needs for the future world, that is with collection and storage of concentrated foods, medical supplies, machinery, and all sorts of means for establishing communications from man to man.

(In parentheses, however, I may mention that along this line of thinking I had the privilege, as a trustee of the Pestalozzi Foundation of America and as its one-time chairman of the board, to cooperate with its founder and president, Mr. H. C. Honegger, in extended work for war orphan villages and institutes all over the globe, which I consider as one of the most outstanding efforts towards the construction of a sound unified world in the sense described in the introduction to this book. The Pestalozzi Foundation, which owes its success entirely to the genius of Mr. Honegger, has been guided very much by morphological thought, although perhaps not consciously so. Because of its outstanding contribution towards universal understanding I intend to describe its activities more fully in my forthcoming book *Everyone a Genius.*)

Even for a busy individual there remained, however, one obvious possibility for making an early contribution towards the reconstruction, after the war, of the world, which certainly would need schools, colleges and libraries to educate and train scientists, physicians, and engineers, who would have to get to work rebuilding what had been destroyed and lost. After some thought it became clear to me that along this line of endeavour even an individual scholar could contribute much, single-handedly, without actually unduly neglecting his regular duties at his university and without compromising his contributions towards winning the war. Indeed, a thorough morphological survey indicated that loads of essential scientific journals could be gathered and stored for future distribution at no cost whatever except for some efficient and fast work by myself and the use of my car, as well as much labor of sorting, packing, and registering by dozens of friends of mine, ladies and gentlemen all, who were eager to do something for the world, but who could find no adequate place to contribute technically to the war effort.

Applying the method of the morphological box to the procurement (and later to the shipment) of scientific journals and textbooks proved to be successful beyond our wildest expectations. The following standard morphological procedures produced the desired results.

FIRST STEP: FORMULATION OF THE PROBLEM

For the purpose of replacing the materials in various scientific libraries in many countries that may be expected to be destroyed or lost through bombing and other acts of war, a collection is to be started of scientific journals and books, which after the war are to be distributed to the institutions most in need. No financial funds, however, are available for this action.

SECOND STEP: SCRUTINY OF THE ESSENTIAL PARAMETERS OF THE PROBLEM

For example, the *first* determining circumstance or, as the mathematicians express it, the first parameter P_1 refers to the type of journal desired and has the components P_{1a}, where the index a runs from 1 to k (k is a whole number, say 7 or 13, as we shall determine later on). As we have stated, the parameter P_1 describes the various individual journals by the second subscript a of the components P_{1a}, which represents the total number of issues of that particular journal (a) during some definite year Y_r. A refinement of the morphological analysis is introduced by establishing separate morphological boxes (or magazine flow charts) for every year Y. For purposes of illustration we assume that we are interested here only in those journals issued during one particular year, say $Y = 1943$. The components P_{1a} thus represent the following objects:

P_{11} = all issues of the *Physical Review* for 1943,
P_{12} = all issues of *Science* for 1943,
P_{13} = all issues of *Helvetica Physica Acta* for 1943,
P_{14} = all issues of *Experientia* for 1943,
and so on.

The *second* parameter P_2 identifies the *first* subscriber or receiver of one or more issues of the scientific journals P_{1a}. This subscriber may be an individual, a factory, a university library, a public library, the patent office, or others. The components P_{2b} thus represent for instance: P_{21} = Mr. X, P_{22} = Mr. Y, P_{28} = library of the California Institute of Technology, P_{29} = Library of the University of California at Los Angeles, $P_{2,10}$ = Library of the Aerojet General Corporation and so on.

For a comprehensive review of the values of P_{2b} it is advisable not to consider each individual subscriber separately, but to work with statistical averages that refer to professional groups or groups of institutions, such as professors or patent lawyers as separate groups, and engineers, industrial consultants, physicians, writers, news bureaus, aeroplane factories, rocket engine factories, chemical factories, scientific academies, and so on as other groups. The *third* parameter P_3 stands for all of the second owners of journals or textbooks P_{1a}. This parameter therefore has the following types of components:

P_{31} = son or daughter of a first subscriber (P_{1a}).
P_{32} = collaborator, associate or friend of a first subscriber.
P_{33} = widow, or estate of a first subscriber.
P_{34} = some general beneficiary or repository that receives donations, such as university libraries, public libraries, etc.

The following parameters, P_4, P_5, P_6 and so on, are identical in character with P_3, since the journals may go from hand to hand for some time until they come to rest at the locations indicated by the components of the parameter P_e (final end), which are of the following types:

P_{e1} = total destruction of some of the issues through fire, water damage, ultimate wear and tear, and so on.
P_{e2} = pulp and paper mill.
P_{e3} = storage in some attic, garage or cellar.
P_{e4} = permanent resting place in private, industrial, governmental or scientific library.

For our purposes the following morphological box or flow chart must therefore be studied (see Fig. 24).

THIRD STEP: ESTABLISHMENT AND STUDY OF THE FLOW CHART OF THE SCIENTIFIC AND TECHNICAL JOURNALS TO BE COLLECTED

In the chart shown we circle a definite component P_{1j} in the first row, which represents all of the issues of a given journal j for the year Y (we repeat that a flow chart has been constructed for every year). In each of the following rows we also circle respectively one single component P_{uv}. Interconnecting all of these circled components we construct a chain, shown in Figure 24 for

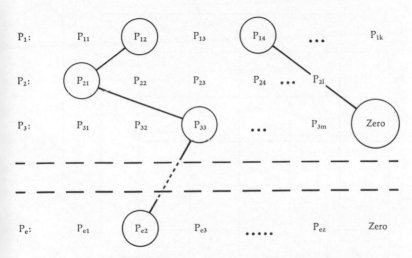

Fig. 24. *Flow chart of scientific and technical journals.*

instance as $[P_{12}, P_{21}, P_{33}, \ldots \ldots P_{e2}]$ which represents the "history" of a fraction $\alpha \cdot P_{1j}$ of the total number P_{1j} of the particular journal j which were issued in the year Y. The sum over all of the flow lines or chains which start from P_{1j} there are $l \cdot m \cdot \ldots \cdot z$ of them—gives the sum $\Sigma \alpha = 1$ since we have thus included the flow lines of all of the issues of the journal j for the year Y.

Instead of the flow chart shown in Figure 24, mathematicians may prefer to arrange or to house the various parameter components P_{uv} which characterize the totality of the possible solutions of a given problem in a multidimensional morphological box of e dimensions. If for purposes of illustration we restrict ourselves to three parameters ($e = 3$), our morphological box would be three-dimensional, and it could thus be represented as a chest of

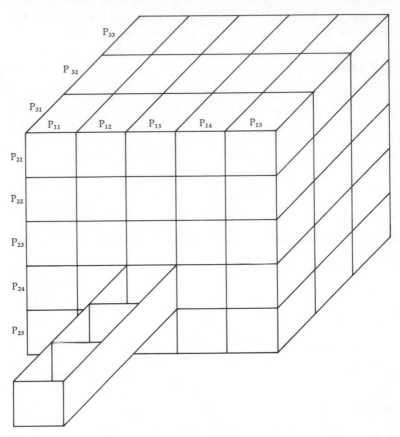

Fig. 25. *Simple three-dimensional morphological box with 25 drawers and 75 compartments containing the combinations or chains of the parameter components P_{uv} which characterize the various journals and their successive owners. The particular drawer that appears pulled out in the drawing contains in its three compartments, from front to back, the three flow lines* [P_{13}, P_{24}, P_{31}], [P_{13}, P_{24}, P_{32}], *and* [P_{13}, P_{24}, P_{33}].

twenty-five drawers with three partitions or compartments in each $(e = 3; l = 5, m = 5$ and $z = 3)$. This reduced morphological box or chest thus contains seventy-five compartments, in each of which we find the description of one flow line of some of the issues of a specific scientific journal.

In the simple morphological box shown in Figure 25, all flow lines that start from the component P_{13}, representing the total number of issues of the scientific journals of the type 3, are contained in the five drawers, with fifteen compartments, that lie vertically below the coordinate designation P_{13}.

To make our scheme entirely realistic we must assign to each of the parameters P_3 to P_e, also respectively, one zero component, as they appear at the end of the lower rows of Figure 24. It may indeed happen that some issues of our journals come to their final resting places before they have reached those potential resting places indicated in the last row e.

Except for special wishes occasionally expressed by the representatives of the war-devastated libraries I always endeavoured to collect the greatest number of the most valuable journals and especially those of small issues. In 1942 I therefore carried out a preliminary statistical-morphological analysis of the complex of the flow charts discussed above. This analysis was continually improved as I gained more experience and knowledge about the habits of the various donors and publishing agencies as well as the successive owners of the desired journals. This type of procedure, which is practiced more or less successfully by all men of good sense, can, however, be most efficiently systematized through the morphological approach. In mathematics and theoretical physics it is widely applied and well known as the *method of successive approximations*.

FOURTH AND FIFTH STEPS IN THE APPLICATION OF THE METHOD OF THE MORPHOLOGICAL BOX

In the course of a decade, from about 1940 to 1950, I analysed, as already mentioned, all the flow lines of the desired scientific journals contained in our morphological chest, improving the evaluation step by step as new experiences were gathered. This fourth step enabled me to recognize those points along the flow lines where interception appeared most promising. In this way the fifth step of choosing optimal solutions to our problem could be realized, and we invariably obtained numerous issues of scientific journals and textbooks free of charge.

The method of the successive approximation is nothing but a part of the procedure of complete morphological field coverage described in the preceding chapter. Starting from a sufficient number of well-established pegs of knowledge and experience, as well as using readily available materials, one constructs first a suitable supporting framework from which to start for all further investigations. Filling the voids in this framework in successive steps, one succeeds eventually in exploring and exploiting all the relevant and initially unknown territories. If the whole framework is dynamic rather than static, that is if the complex of facts and phenomena in question is evolving, the method of "feedback" must be coupled with the method of successive approximation, because circumstances which might have had certain definite qualitative and quantitative aspects at one time must be re-evaluated on the basis of findings gained at a later time. The successful application of the method of field coverage to complexes of objects and of phenomena that change in time therefore demands great flexibility and a total lack of bias, that is, absolute refrainment from prevaluation in the use of the *methods of successive approximation and continuous feedback*.

Since I had no funds at all for the purpose, and therefore had to secure the desired scientific journals free of charge, all flow lines that terminated in the parameter component P_{e_4} had to be disregarded. With this in mind it remained to intercept all other flow lines as near as possible to those components of P_4 that appear in them, since at these particular locations the market value of the journals generally approached zero. These considerations led in their practical application to astounding successes, inasmuch as I obtained in the end more material free of charge than I could hope to handle and to transport to the many intended locations overseas. A few examples of advantageous points of interception along the flow lines for purposes of the diversion of scientific journals to war-stricken scientific libraries are sketched briefly here.

One of the most promising points of interception lies at the parameter component (or the matrix element) $P_{2,10}$. In the case of a great airplane factory, such as the Douglas Aircraft Company in Santa Monica, California, or a rocket factory like the Aerojet General Corporation in Azusa, California, a telephone call suffices to ascertain that several copies of many scientific and technical journals have been subscribed to by these concerns. One also learns that of these copies, there may be as many as twenty each, only a few are being retained and bound in volumes to be permanently incorporated in the respective companies' libraries. The remaining issues, after some time, which often amounted to one or two years, became available to our collection, one of the reasons being that many factories often do not have enough free space available to store great numbers of unbound journals conveniently.

Further rich sources of scientific journals and surplus textbooks are to be found at those institutions that are the most likely recipients of literature left by scientists, engineers, and physicians after their death. Many of these professionals store their journals during their whole lifetime, and their widows or those in charge of their estates do not know what to do with such accumulations except to turn them over to some public library, to the chamber of commerce, to a university club, or even to the automobile club. These institutions either already possess the necessary copies themselves, or they have no use at all for the gifts sent them, so that many of them were quite eager to let our Committee for Aid to Warstricken Scientific Libraries haul away much valuable material.

A third source of supply was found in the form of certain widely scattered issues, which seem to be of no value to anybody until they have been collected and properly assembled. I am referring to those single copies of scientific magazines that contain a contribution by this or that scholar who subsequently automatically or upon request receives one or two complimentary copies of the issue in which his article appeared. Experience has shown that very few of the authors have any use for such odd numbers of journals received. This happened for instance to me and to my colleagues at the Mount Wilson and Palomar Observatories. Most of us were already subscribers to the important scientific journals to which we sent our articles for printing. Furthermore our observatories distribute hundreds of individual reprints of our articles to astronomers all over the world. Individual complimentary copies were therefore piled away by the various authors in some corners of their respective offices, and they were only too happy to let me remove them. I thus remember that, on one of the first days of my action in 1941, I collected in this way eighty-three complete volumes of the *Astrophysical Journal*, which today represent a value of at least one thousand dollars in the United States and considerably more on location overseas where they are now in use.

A fourth vulnerable point is to be found with the old retired gentlemen of science and technology who are easy to talk to since they often feel neglected. Most of them will cooperate gladly with younger colleagues in any effort to establish a unified community of science all over the world. My sincere thanks go to many of them for their contributions to our collection for the war-stricken scientific libraries. Also, thanks to their passing the word, our committee eventually became so well known that journals were contributed almost automatically, without our having to make any further time-consuming efforts in solicitation.

As an auxiliary result of the activities of the Committee for Aid to Warstricken Scientific Libraries, Pasadena, many of my collaborators familiarized themselves with the theory and practice of the morphological approach. They not only learned of its specific application to the collection, handling, and shipment of huge quantities of scientific journals and books, but were prepared for its application in later years to a multitude of large-scale problems. As to our collection for the war-stricken libraries, some of the most resourceful collaborators helped me in particular with the solution of the following two additional and most necessary tasks.

First, all of the journals had to be sorted, packed, registered, and properly assigned to the various countries that could most efficiently use them and a very voluminous correspondence had to be handled. *Second,* the most difficult problem of arranging for free transportation from Pasadena to Los Angeles Harbor and then to the recipients in Europe, Asia, and Africa had to be arranged.

The study and occupation with these two problems proved most illuminating, regarding both its technical and, especially, its human and psychological aspects. The combined wits of all of us, as well as morphological planning, were necessary to achieve the desired results. We probably compounded our difficulties by insisting that the recipients of our shipment show good faith and expecting them to help as much as they could, particularly in arranging for the best use of the journals received. The Institut d'Astrophysique in Paris for instance, which is associated with the Observatoire de Paris, had all of the journals that were sent to them bound immediately, so we knew that we had sent the material to the right place. Likewise it became clear that we were dealing with serious and reliable people when Chiang Kai Shek's minister of education arrived in Pasadena, pulled up his shirt sleeves and helped us packing, while calling up all of the Chinese students in the neighborhood and inviting them to do likewise.

To enter here into all of the ramifications of our project is of course impossible. A book should perhaps eventually be written about our experiences, the analysis of which might be of value, especially to those scientists who are interested in the services science can and should render to the world in general. A few of these experiences may here be briefly mentioned.

The over-all results of our efforts were the following: Scientific and technical journals, as well as textbooks, were collected, principally in and around Pasadena, California, and were ultimately presented to a number of war-stricken scientific libraries overseas. The total value of all of the materials delivered, based on the sales prices at the actual locations, amounted to about one million dollars. The recipients of our largest shipments were the following: The scientific allocation committee of the government of the Philippines; the Severance Medical College at Seoul, as well as various universities of the Republic of South Korea; the Naval Academy of South Korea; the Physikalisch-Technische Bundesanstalt in Braunschweig, which took care of the proper distribution of all of the shipments to various universities and technical colleges in West Germany; the university of Caën in Normandy, France, which city had been almost entirely destroyed during the invasion; the Institut d'Astrophysique in Paris; the Centre National de la Recherche Scientifique in Paris (for their library at the castle of Gif); the National Taiwan University of Free China in Teipeh, Taiwan (Formosa); the Teacher's Institute in Teipeh, Formosa; the Max Planck Institut fuer Stroemungsforschung in Goettingen (for further distribution among the local scientific libraries); several voluminous shipments to the center of the Deutsche Forschungsgemeinschaft in Bad Godesberg near Bonn for distribution among all German universities; the Observatoire de Nice, to assist it in its reconstruction and rejuvenation, as well as smaller shipments to Nigeria, the American University in Beirut (Lebanon); Japan; and universities in Brazil, Mexico, and so on.

The success of the action by the Committee for Aid to War-stricken Scientific Libraries, Pasadena, proved before all that even a lone scientist, although he may not have any funds at his disposal whatever, can contribute materially to the unification of a tragically confused and strife-torn world. It is imagination, morphological planning, and indomitable perseverance that count.

Much experience was gathered, which promises to be of considerable value in the conduct of future similar projects. It was particularly gratifying that so many large concerns would lend a helping hand and that so many individuals would contribute work and sweat to an enterprise that could not possibly yield any remuneration or any particular recognition, except the satisfaction of having done a job well and the belated thanks we must not fail to extend to all participants more or less anonymously. Concerning the support we occasionally enjoyed on a large scale, I must mention before all the United States Defense Department and in particular the United States Navy. For instance, my old friend Dan A. Kimball, when he was Secretary of the Navy in 1952, put at my disposal for a few weeks a staff of officers of the Navy, as well as packers and secretaries who expeditiously sorted, registered, packed, and crated about fifteen tons of journals from my collection, which were subsequently transported on Navy vessels to Formosa and Korea. Likewise the United States State Department extended to us valuable assistance in connection with President Truman's "Point Four Plan." Furthermore, some large commercial concerns, such as the Compagnie Générale Transatlantique (French Line), the Shell Oil Company, and others, offered to ship our boxes free of charge. And last but not least, towards the intended termination of our activities I received a grant of ten thousand dollars from the Ford Foundation to help me liquidate the whole project as expeditiously as possible until the year of 1957, since the work load became so heavy that I would have had to neglect other essential tasks. This hope for absolute liquidation, however, has remained more or less a pious wish to this very day. Indeed, it proved practically impossible to start refusing all requests from one day to the next or, for that matter to stop the influx of material abruptly. The demands for free scientific literature and technical books are still coming in at a great rate, but unfortunately I have not succeeded in finding an energetic young colleague who would be prepared to continue my project. Inquiries in this direction at UNESCO in Paris and at some of the respectvie offices of the United Nations in New York also have not produced any tangible results. These failures represent the only major disappointment, particularly because they indicate that science, seen from the point of view of the practical social philosopher or the morphologist, is as yet in its very infancy and has not clearly realized its duties and responsibilities towards the human community, or at any rate scientists are not willing to live up to them.

On the other hand we had some most encouraging experiences

with many students and assistants, as well as private individuals outside of the scientific circles, who were quite willing to co-operate, at least in the many small chores that had to be performed. The most valuable result of our project perhaps is that many men and women of good will came together and learned to know each other, all individuals who are ready to cooperate unselfishly in any future tasks of sociological import, and they acquired the practical experience and skills to make further valuable contributions towards the buildup of a sound world.

The most important, and I choose to stress this, *by far the most important achievement* from our efforts on behalf of the war-stricken scientific libraries lies in the conviction gained that it is not money and might that are the most essential elements for our goal to establish constructive relations among the various quarreling and warring nations and our endeavours to reconcile the conflicting ideologies: We must, before all, inspire men to see each other as friends. The time we have left to achieve this has become short, very short. But no true morphologist will ever give up and admit that it is too late. Obviously, many enormous obstacles stand in the way, some of the major ones being acid reactions to the century-old inhuman and idiotic treatment so many peoples suffered at the hands of the colonial powers. As the Americans learned, to their great astonishment, the distrust of these races that were miserably suppressed for so long by the "whites" cannot be dispelled even by unlimited financial and material aid, if this is not intimately coupled with sincere efforts to establish relations between man and man and the clear intention to build a world in which there are no master races and backward or even slave peoples. During a flight from New York to Zurich I saw a full-page statement in *The New York Times* of June 12, 1956, which had been placed by Mr. Basil Brewer, editor of the New Bedford (Massachusetts) *Standard Times* which asked pointedly "Why does the World hate America?" This article states, "Since the war America has distributed to the World 52,287,000,000 dollars of which 45,107,000,000 were *gifts pure and simple*. With this sum we could have rebuilt every road in the Country, or created a superaviation, far beyond Russia's ability to compete." The same article claims that the principal weakness of Americans is that they do not dare look the world straight in the face and express their convictions and opinions succinctly and unmistakably in word and deed. For instance, Mr. Brewer says that both the United States government and the American people have clearly stated that all suppressed peoples must be given their freedom, but the United States representatives at the United Nations have not resolutely fought for this principle and have often acquiesced to sickening compromises and plain injustices.

We must add here the second and most important observation and warning: We are not likely to succeed in unifying the world as long as the Americans and the British, or for that matter any other people, feel and act as if they are better and superior to all others. For instance, the remarkable success General Douglas MacArthur had in the Philippines and in Japan is to be credited largely to the fact that he treated the coloured peoples and the whites strictly as equals, and in his own way, he sincerely tried to assist all of them in the realization of their specific and very own potentialities and characteristics.

One other most rewarding aspect of our action for the war-stricken scientific libraries was that no Korean, Chinese, Filipino, Arab, or Negro ever acted or reacted in any way as if we had not treated him as our absolute equal. President Chiang Kai-Shek, who had often had to work with little help or none, as we did with our project, expressed this very neatly. He solved the problem of thanking us for the shipments received at the Taiwan National University in a most ingenious way. He sent me a parchment scroll on which a row of Chinese characters indicated that the two names (written in Chinese) that appeared at the two ends of this row, namely his and mine, are connected by a bridge of culture.

From all of these experiences morphologists must conclude that sociological problems, and especially those on an international scale, can be solved best if everyone helps all others to develop their own unique potentialities. And perhaps these problems can actually be solved only if all individuals and races are being given the opportunity and means to realize their own unique genius. Science and education will here find their most important and most noble tasks. It would be tragic if the scholars as well as the professionals in all fields did not avail themselves of this perhaps last chance for collective action. They need not fear that such action will be in vain. Any unselfish and well-planned initiative of this character will certainly find all-around recognition, approval, and appreciation as we have experienced it again and again in our small-scale efforts. Among the testimonies which confirm this conclusion is a letter from the president of the German Federal Republic, Mr. Heinrich Luebke and part of an article by Dr. Gisela von Busse of the central office of the Deutsche Forschungsgemeinschaft in Bad Godesberg, which appeared in the library journal Zeitschrift fuer Biblothekwesen, Vol. 4, issue 1, (1958).

Item 6:
American Book Aid: Committee for Aid to Warstricken Scientific Libraries. With this last great action the circle closes itself. Just as the American Library Association the Committee for Aid to Warstricken Scientific Libraries which was founded at the beginning of the War has since that time started actions for the alleviation of the needs of libraries all over the world. In analogy to the attitude adopted by CARE, the willingness to help, be it of the individual scholar or of a scientific or technical institution and libraries was relied upon, and during many years, magazines and books, primarily on pure and applied science, were collected. This was so much an action from man to man, scholar to scholar, that the founder of this enterprise, Professor F. Zwicky of the California Institute of Technology and astronomer at the Mount Wilson and Palomar Observatories, helped by the members of his family and by some of his closest friends, was not only initiator and organizer, but also collector, distributor and even packer, all in one. Many a German professor who visited the world famous Mount Wilson and Palomar Observatories and at the same time became acquainted with this collection received as a result some valuable gifts for his own uni-

versity. Not counting any of these smaller actions, four large shipments arrived in the Federal Republic of Germany: the first (40 boxes or about 4 metric tons) in 1949 at the Physikalisch-Technische Bundesanstalt in Braunschweig, the second (16 boxes = 1.5 tons) at the Max-Planck-Institut fuer Strömungs-forschung in Göttingen and the third and fourth (40 boxes each of together about 8 tons) in 1957 and 1958 to the Deutsche Forschungsgemeninschaft in Godesberg, while a fifth and final one of about 50 boxes is being prepared for shipment in 1959. The contents of all of these boxes were distributed to those institutions in Germany that needed them most and could best use them. If even today, 13 years after the end of the war, the rest of the collection still has not left Pasadena, although Professor Zwicky already in May 1950 expressed the wish to liquidate his enterprise, one realizes with shocking clearness the extent of the physical, moral and temperamental effort required for the successful realization of such large-scale book-aid actions.

For the most part it was a question of collecting extended and continuous sets of scientific journals; only the latest shipments contained of necessity more and more individual issues, always, however, of the most important and most needed magazines. How welcome even scattered single copies are, becomes evident from the requests received by the Deutsche Forschungs-gemeinschaft in the form of "Duplicate Lists." Never before, during the period of the NOTGEMEINSCHAFT (Emergency Aid Agency) and the REICHSAUSTAUSCHSTELLE (German Federal Book Exchange Service) which preceded the establishment of the Deutsche Forschungsgemeinschaft, have even the large university libraries responded to the duplicate lists with so many requests as now, after the American material sent by the Committee for Aid to Warstricken Scientific Libraries (with headquarters in Pasadena, California) has become available.

The only reward which the organizers of the aid action in Pasadena enjoyed lies in the knowledge of having done something worthwhile and useful. We the recipients, however, shall never forget the trying times when we were cut off from the outside world, and we shall always remember that the re-establishment of the free give and take of thought and of the results of research is in large measure to be credited to the untiring and unselfish efforts of individuals in former enemy countries. This we wish to acknowledge emphatically and in all sincerity in order to thank those who gave so much of themselves.

DER PRÄSIDENT
DER
BUNDESREPUBLIK DEUTSCHLAND

Bonn, den 11. September 1961

Sehr geehrter Herr Professor Zwicky !

Wie mir die Deutsche Forschungsgemeinschaft berichtet, ist nun auch die letzte der fünf großen Büchersendungen des "California Institute of Technology" in der Bundesrepublik eingetroffen. Die Bücher und Zeitschriften wurden bereits an verschiedene kriegsgeschädigte deutsche Bibliotheken verteilt.

Ihnen als dem Initiator und tätigen Organisator der großzügigen Hilfsaktion und dem von Ihnen gegründeten Komitee möchte ich daher heute meinen aufrichtigen Dank aussprechen. Weitblickend erkannten Sie schon während des Krieges die kommenden Nöte der Bibliotheken in den kriegsbetroffenen Ländern und riefen zu einer Hilfsaktion auf. Ihr Appell an die Gebefreudigkeit der Forscher, der Institute und der Bibliotheken

Herrn   -2-
Professor Dr. F. Z w i c k y
Vorsitzender des Committee for Aid
to War Stricken Scientific Libraries
California Institut of Technology
1201 East California
P a s a d e n a / California

in den Vereinigten Staaten hatte den überwälti-
genden Erfolg, daß in den vergangenen Jahren
171 Kisten mit wertvollem wissenschaftlichen
Material nach Deutschland verschifft und hier
verteilt werden konnten.

Wie in den Nachkriegsjahren die Care-Pakete
aus den Vereinigten Staaten weit über ihren ma-
teriellen Wert hinaus im deutschen Volk wieder
Mut und Glauben an menschliche Hilfsbereitschaft
weckten und den ersten Anlaß zur Überwindung der
Not gaben, so hat Ihre Spende in den deutschen
Wissenschaftlern, vor allem auch in der jungen
Generation, die erste neue Hoffnung geweckt und
geholfen, die geistige Not der Isolierung zu über-
winden.

Wir, die Beschenkten, werden diese frühe und
tatkräftige Hilfe nicht vergessen. Sie wird uns
ein Ansporn sein, auch unsererseits über die Gren-
zen hinweg die Solidarität der Forschung in der
freien Welt des Geistes zu bekunden und ihr un-
eigennützig zu dienen.

Genehmigen Sie, Herr Professor, die Versiche-
rung meiner ausgezeichneten Hochachtung.

The President   Bonn, September 11, 1961
of the
German Federal Republic

Dear Professor Zwicky:

The Deutsche Forschungsgemeinschaft informs me that the last of the five large shipments of scientific library materials from the "California Institute of Technology" has now arrived in the Federal Republic. The books and journals have already been distributed among the various German war-stricken scientific libraries.

To you as the initiator and active organizer of this extended aid project and to the Committee founded by you I should like to express my deep-felt thanks. Already during the war you foresaw with remarkable vision the future dire needs of the war-stricken scientific libraries, and you called for long-range action. Your appeal to the good will of your colleagues, institutes and the libraries in the United States of America met with such overpowering success that 171 large cases of valuable scientific journals could be shipped to Germany alone.

Far beyond their material value the CARE packages from the United States of America in the postwar years reawakened in the German people their courage and a belief in human cooperation. Similarly, your aid rekindled among the German scientists, and particularly in the young generation, the first new hope and determination to overcome the effects of the isolation of the war years.

We, the recipients, will not forget this timely and effective aid action, which has inspired us to work unselfishly for the solidarity of research in the free world of the mind.

Accept, dear professor, the assurance of my highest esteem.

Signed: Lübke

In illustration of our thesis that the morphological approach automatically leads to numerous useful extensions of any project which is being worked upon intensively, I wish to mention in parenthesis the history of the *Swiss Forward Teams* in India, Nepal, and other countries. During short visits in Switzerland in 1945 and 1946 I informed some of my young Swiss friends about the activities of the Committee for Aid to Warstricken Scientific Libraries, and I suggested to them that they initiate educational and technical developments in some of the countries asking for such cooperation. It was in particular Dr. Walter Custer, now professor of architecture at the Federal Institute of Technology in Zurich, who took up this idea and organized the so-called Swiss Forward Teams of young Swiss professionals to work in India and in Nepal.* These teams have been in action ever since. The Truman Doctrine in 1949 took up the same idea on a much grander scale and the Peace Corps, a decade later, was modeled along lines similar to those of the Swiss Forward Teams and Swiss Academic Teams, one of whose first projects had been the construction of international war orphan villages, the most typical among them being the world-famous *Pestalozzi Dorf* near Trogen, Switzerland.

Second Application of the Method of the Morphological Box: The Totality of the Interrelations between Physico-Chemical Phenomena; Types of Energy and Energy Transformations

The essence of the world is evolution of matter and energy. The different types of energy and the transformations of one form of energy into another play a decisive role in the events of the universe. Man, from the beginning, has of necessity been interested in these transformations, which he has exploited throughout the millennia and which have enabled him to use the untapped or wasting away potential resources of nature for ever more ex-

---

* For a more detailed account see: *Vom Werden der schweizerischen Entwicklungshilfe. Schweiz. Zeitschr. Für Gemeinnützigkeit*, Vol. 105, issue 1/2, 1966.

tended technological developments and the enrichment of his life.

Considering this all-important role of energy transformations, it is almost unbelievable that neither the physicists nor the engineers have ever attempted an integrated systematic presentation and comprehensive analysis of all of them. It remained for morphological research, which occupies itself in principle with the study of the totality of all possibilities inherent in any set of circumstances, to review, in particular, the totality of all of the conceivable energy transformations. The decisive aspects are the following:

As we have already stated, energy, no matter of what type it may be, is *something* that can either be used to set matter, which is originally at rest, in motion, or it can be applied to stop moving matter. The *first question* to arise is how many kinds of energy actually exist that are capable of exerting on matter the effects just described. It is of course not necessary that this be achieved directly. It will suffice if one type of energy is first converted into another type, which subsequently is transformed into kinetic energy. The *second question* of course concerns the possibilities of putting the various types of energy to good use. That is, how can they serve man to achieve his technological and scientific goals? Parenthetically we must emphasize that science and technology not only occupy themselves with the study and applications of all types of energy, but they are equally interested and dependent on the investigation and production of innumerable materials to be used in architecture, and civil, mechanical, and electrical engineering, in the production of food and clothing, and for applications in the arts and in medicine.

For the present we are here interested only in those technological activities that concern themselves with the production and uses of various types of energy. The study of all forms of energy, of all energy transformations and of the characteristics of all matter in its microscopic, macroscopic and cosmic aggregates represent a topic of major interest to physicists, chemists, and astronomers. As stated, however, we are for the present concerned only with the essential characteristics of the various types of energy and with their significance for the economy and the activities of the world.

The morphologist endeavours to answer both the questions raised above without ever losing sight of the all-important goal of ultimately comprehending all the essential aspects of energy and the characteristics of all possible energy transformations. He is thus interested on the one hand in the historical developments of the uses of energy, and on the other hand he strives to visualize the potentialities inherent in these uses for the future. With these purposes in mind we shall attempt some preliminary reviews of the following subjects: first, the totality of all types of energy; second, the totality of all energy transformations; and third, the almost innumerable multitude of devices that, in one way or another, achieve the many possible conversions of one type of energy into another. This multitude, being so enormous, however, only very little can be said about it in this book. The whole complex of the many aspects of the different types of energy may, in a natural way, be incorporated in the general historical framework discussed in the first chapter. What we there hinted at can here be more succinctly illustrated by a specific example, which confirms our opinion that throughout the millennia enormous progress has been made as a result of the work of many devoted and gifted individual investigators. At the same time much of what had been achieved was wasted again, because criminal misuse went hand in hand with scientific discoveries and technical developments and construction. We must therefore see to it that the men of research, the engineers, the physicians and all scholars and professionals in general, cooperate with one another to ensure the optimal constructive use of all sources of energy and prevent irresponsible individuals and power groups from wasting it for their own selfish or even fiendish purposes. And what is still more important: Scientists and all professionals must collaborate with the general public and work shoulder to shoulder with the ordinary citizen to eliminate all the misuses of energy that in the past have led to a progressive devastation of the wealth and beauty of nature, to the pollution of air and water and to the ever-mounting death toll from automobile traffic, not to mention the numerous attending phenomena of permanent injuries, and all sorts of illnesses, neuroses and psychoses, which arise from the fact that the inner strength of man has not kept pace with scientific and technological progress. And finally, one of the most urgent problems of our age: We cannot allow our world to be endangered or completely annihilated as a result of criminal or irresponsible manipulation of the forces we scientists have recently unleashed through the liberation of atomic energy.

ENERGY AND ITS USES THROUGHOUT HISTORY

The Prescientific Age

Long before it was recognized what the different aspects of energy are and before the subsequent success of scientists in formulating the respective laws of nature, man made many uses for various types of energy. Scientists and laymen alike may enjoy reading about all of these efforts in old records, history books, and encyclopedias. Such a study becomes particularly exciting and rewarding if one also embarks on the search for actual devices used by the ancients for the exploitation of available sources of energy, or better yet if he attempts to reconstruct them from instructions or descriptions found. A considerable number of energy sources and of energy conversions were known to the ancients. Among these we can only mention a few. In doing so we shall always try to contrast energy conversions as they occur by themselves in nature to those that are conducted with the aid of artifacts invented and constructed by man for his specific needs.

Conversions of Kinetic Energy Into Kinetic Energy

Even primitive man must have observed that a body in motion, such as a rolling stone or flowing water, can, on impact, put another body in motion, which was initially at rest. The ancients devised many contrivances to exploit available sources of kinetic energy. Among them the water wheel is the best known, with applications in mills to grind grain and later on to operate saw mills. The water jet reaction (recoil) wheel, now called the Seegner water wheel, must also have been known long ago. This wheel is one of the first forerunners of modern propulsive power plants. In another application, sailboats, the kinetic energy of the winds is being harnessed by the sails to set the boats in motion. The sailboat is therefore another example of a device which converts kinetic energy into kinetic energy.

Conversions of Gravitational Energy Into Kinetic Energy

Early man certainly must also have known that, when sitting on the branch of a tree, he would fall if the branch were to break. Physicists say that in this case gravitational potential energy is being converted into kinetic energy. Analogous conversions are taking place when water starts flowing into the valley, or rain falls out of the atmosphere on the ground or on the ocean, or again when the tides fall. On the other hand, a stone that is thrown vertically eventually loses all its kinetic energy and instead gains or accumulates gravitational potential energy. The same is true for the *rising* tide. A man on skis can set himself in motion through the conversion of gravitational potential energy into kinetic energy and thus gain the lowlands more rapidly than by walking. A mechanical catapult is another contrivance that allows us to lauch a missile through the transformation of gravitational energy into kinetic energy.

The Conversion of Elastic Energy Into Kinetic Energy

Whenever primitive man moved through the bushes he bent their branches to both sides. When they were released an instant later, they may have hit those who followed him in the face, not to their pleasure I should think. A physicist would say that the kinetic energy of the moving man was transformed into elastic potential energy of the branches and this, on release, was converted into kinetic energy of these branches. Primitive man also invented an artifact that cleverly makes use of this conversion. Indeed the launching of an arrow from a taut bow or from a cross bow makes use of this principle. The conversion into motion of the elastic energy stored in the wound up spring of a watch is another example.

Conversion of Heat Into Kinetic Energy and Vice Versa

Primitive man must also have noticed that if a moving body is stopped, heat is being produced. This might have occurred to him for instance while grinding stones or drilling wood and especially when igniting some dry spongy material by means of hitting two flint stones together. He probably also saw that in a fire, parts of the branches may be exploding and sparks will fly, that is bodies will be set in motion through the action of the heat. The same can be seen when water starts bubbling in a pot which is being heated. But it was thousands of years before man learned to really understand the processes involved and invent and build devices that achieve the transformation of heat into kinetic energy with an acceptable degree of efficiency. The principal reason for this slow process probably lies in the fact that heat, in contradistinction to motion has a much more elusive character, and it cannot be manipulated as easily. Nevertheless, Heron of Alexandria (around 150 to 100 B.C.) had already constructed a wheel, consisting of bent tubes, which is set in motion by the recoil of steam flowing through them and being ejected from them. Therefore, Heron's steam wheel jet may perhaps be the first predecessor of modern thermal propulsive power plants.

Only much later did James Watt (1736–1819) invent a device that can convert heat into kinetic energy with very much greater efficiency and on a much larger scale than Heron's wheel. Like Heron, Watt in his steam engine used the heat to evaporate water first and then introduced it into a cylinder in which it expanded, setting in motion a movable piston within this cylinder and a flywheel attached to the piston.

Conversion of Chemical Energy Into Heat

According to the old myths we are indebted to Prometheus for the most important and most common conversion of chemical energy into heat, inasmuch as he stole the fire from the solar carriage of the gods and brought it down to earth. Today we know that heat produced by any combustion is actually the heat of reaction, which is liberated through the oxydation of a fuel such as wood by the oxygen of the air.

In order to make the most efficient use of this energy transfer for heating their abodes, for cooking and for the heat treatment and easier workability of metals and glass, the ancients invented ovens, furnaces and contrivances of all sorts. A systematic search for such artifacts and their reconstruction in the form of models, for purposes of exhibition and teaching, has been and continues to be of the greatest interest to archaeologists, historians, collectors, and laymen alike.

A typical and most important breakthrough and development was initiated long ago by the Chinese through their invention of gunpowder and various mixtures that on ignition can produce fireworks. These fast-reacting mixtures of the Chinese represent the original prototypes of modern explosives and rocket propellants, inasmuch as they contain in themselves the correct proportions of fuels (coal dust and sulfur) as well as oxydizers (saltpeter) to sustain a complete chemical reaction which detonatively generates hot gases at high pressure, and thus an explosion, without making any use of the oxygen of the air.

Conversion of Chemical Energy Into Kinetic Energy

This is the conversion that for man and animal is by far the most important, since without it we could not move at all. The living cells, by means of a series of complicated processes, which even today we do not fully understand, and which we can not reproduce on a practical scale, manage to oxydize the food stuffs that are being consumed and transform the liberated chemical energy into kinetic (and elastic potential) energy. Amazingly enough, all of these conversions take place at essentially constant temperature, a feat accomplished through the reaction of certain enzymes or organic ferments with oxygen on the one hand and with the foodstuffs taken in by the body on the other hand.

As another long-known invention of man that achieves the transformation of chemical energy into kinetic energy we must mention here once more the black gunpowder and other mixtures used by the Chinese, either as explosives or as slower reagents for the purpose of launching various types of projectiles. It is important to emphasize that in all these applications the reaction products of the propellants are generated at high temperatures, and that partly because of this fact, only a small fraction of the liberated energy (or rather free energy) of reaction is converted into useful kinetic energy. It must further be emphasized that until now, and using the most modern technical means available, we have succeeded in only a very limited measure in converting chemical energy isothermally into kinetic energy. The performance of the living cells in oxydizing the food consumed by man and animal and producing this mechanical energy at an almost constant temperature must therefore be considered as a minor miracle whose realization by means of artifacts will be accomplished eventually only as the result of untiring efforts of the most imaginative men of research.

The discussion given in the preceding of the aspects of a specific type of conversion of energy as it occurs in nature and as man may actually realize it clearly illuminates the peculiar fact that nature can do things easily which man is incapable of duplicating. On the other hand, man has already mastered numerous energy conversions occurring in nature but he has done that in ways which yield a very much higher efficiency.

Conversion of Chemical Energy Into Chemical Energy

This type of conversion obviously plays a most important and decisive role, in the world of both plants and animals, as well as in the world of man; numerous processes in all sorts of organisms are activated through the use of many of the raw materials available on the surface of the Earth, including minerals, air, and water, which are introduced as reagents into various reactions producing innumerable new compounds and thus potential chemical energy. Scientists are always amazed to discover with what ease such conversions of chemical energy proceed almost automatically, after changing only slightly the ambient conditions of pressure and temperature. We must, in this connection, again and again marvel at the immense number of carbohydrates, proteins and an incredible variety of other complex chemical compounds living cells are producing, most of which are probably still unknown to science (not to mention our incapability of synthesizing them in the laboratory).

The multitude of mainly inorganic chemical reactions and conversions of energy, which have taken place billions of years ago during the formation and growth of the Earth's crust, represent another almost inexhaustible field of research for geophysicists and geochemists. How the various silicates, carbonates, nitrides, and the rest of the minerals were actually produced still remains largely unknown. In contradistinction it should be emphasized that the astrophysicists expect to know more about the physico-chemical conditions within the sun and possibly the chemistry of the big planets like Jupiter and Saturn than they do about *Inner Space*, that is the interior of the Earth. As a parallel to this rather disturbing fact it must of course be pointed out that it will probably prove far more difficult for us to see, communicate, penetrate, and travel through inner space than it is to reach the planets.

From the beginning man and animal had to rely entirely on the various foodstuffs produced by the plants, without which they could not have existed. This possibility opens itself to us only now. Throughout the millennia man gradually learned also to breed the most useful plants and improve their yield without actually knowing which energy conversions and chemical reactions play the decisive role.

Conversion of Radiative Energy Into Chemical Energy and Vice Versa

The Swiss naturalist Charles Bonnet (1720–93) and the Dutch physician Jan Ingenhousz (1730–99) first discovered that earth, water, and air alone do not suffice for the growth of plants, but that the action of light is needed as well. I do not know, however, which investigator first discovered that many of the substances produced in plants represent chemical compounds of higher potential energy content than the raw materials used and that heat and light must have been introduced to achieve such beneficiation and upgrading of low-grade materials. For example, how chlorophyll so efficiently makes use of visual light with a wavelength close to that of the spectral intensity maximum of the radiation from the sun is not yet clearly understood even today. We only know that this light serves to decompose water and carbondioxide and liberate oxygen, which then is used for the synthesis of complex compounds. In passing it may be mentioned that we have made many uses of the conversion of radiation into chemical (potential) energy, for instance in the blackening of photographic emulsions, or in bleaching, colouring, and so on, by incident light. But no truly large-scale technical applications of the transformation of light into chemical energy have as yet been achieved, although they would be of the greatest importance in view of the immense amounts of solar radiation that remain unused and wasted.

The reverse of the conversions described above takes place in chemiluminescence and appears in nature in the well-known glowing bacteria, fireflies, and jellyfish.

Additional Conversions of Energy That Occur in Nature

A keen and persevering observer will succeed in discovering in nature most of the energy conversions known to science. We leave it to the reader and his imagination to survey the field of natural phenomena. To start him on his way we offer the following trite and well-known facts: The radiation from the sun heats the material bodies; the motion of the meteors through the atmosphere generates light; contact or friction between certain substances and their subsequent separation causes the accumulation of electric charges and the generation of sparks; release of the elastic energy in rubber bands, for instance, will generally liberate (but occasionally also absorb) heat and can generate electricity;

water in capillary tubes may be sucked up to a height of several meters against the action of gravity; a magnet may set iron, nickel, cobalt, or actually any matter in motion; and so on. As stated, there are hundreds of other natural phenomena, which involve conversions of one form of energy into another, for which laymen and scientists may be interested to look.

Energy in the Age of Science

As a consequence of the scientific investigation and mathematical formulation of the laws of mechanics and of gravitation by Galileo (1564–1642), Newton (1643–1727), and their great successors (Lagrange, Euler, Laplace, and others), a development of spiraling acceleration began. As some of the most important results of science during the past three centuries the following might be registered: First and foremost, ever more profound knowledge was gained on the microscopic, macroscopic, and cosmic aspects of the world. The universe revealed itself as being of a quite incredible complexity, and in spite of the enormous store of information already accumulated, we now know that we have made only a very meager beginning. On the other hand it is probable that scientists have succeeded in identifying a major proportion of the various types of energy and all of the possible energy transformations. In addition to the ten different forms of energy E_i to be discussed later, we suspect that at least three additional ones might eventually emerge, which respectively relate to gravitational waves or gravitons, to a possible variable zero point energy of space itself, and to some new phenomena associated with the elementary particles of matter. Since we have succeeded in mathematically strictly formulating the laws governing the various aspects of the mentioned energy transformations, the engineers have been supplied with the basic means to exploit energy constructively in all its manifestations for the enrichment of man's life, or as the case may be, to waste or misuse it for destructive purposes. The unleashing of practically unlimited amounts of energy through the progress made in nuclear physics represents perhaps the greatest and most dangerous and revolutionary event in human history because it has not been accompanied by a deepening of human insight or an establishment of sounder relations between man and man, nor has there been any evidence that any of the pathological and vicious aberrations of the human mind have been dispelled, sublimated or neutralized to a degree commensurate with the technological developments. Since we now approach the climax of this revolution it will be our most urgent task to spare no effort towards the absolute control of the liberated atomic energy and the prevention of its use for destructive purposes.

In their exploration and analysis of the nature of all forms of energy the men of research during the eighteenth and nineteenth centuries discovered the electrical and magnetic types of energy, as well as the physical and chemical actions of light or electromagnetic radiation, actually a combination of variable electric and magnetic fields, which for purposes of convenience, however, we shall register as a separate entity. These three types of energy must be added to those of motion, heat, elasticity, chemical reaction, and gravitation, which we have already discussed.

The twentieth century then brought us atomic or nuclear energy, as well as the famous idea of Einstein's (and independently of the Austrian physicist Hasenoehrl) of the rest energy mc^2 of matter, which is, so to speak, stored in every mass m, and which, in the course of the total annihilation of this mass, is liberated as electromagnetic radiation or as "kinetic energy" of certain corpuscles, neutrinos for instance. The letter c in mc^2 represents the velocity of light $= 300,000$ kilometers per second (or equal to thirty billion centimeters per second).

For practical purposes physicists today distinguish between ten types of energy which we propose to designate symbolically as follows: $E_1 =$ kinetic energy, $E_2 =$ elastic energy, $E_3 =$ gravitational energy, $E_4 =$ heat, $E_5 =$ electrical energy, $E_6 =$ magnetic energy, $E_7 =$ chemical energy, $E_8 =$ electromagnetic radiation (light), $E_9 =$ nuclear energy (in the vernacular called atomic energy), $E_{10} =$ rest energy of matter.

Referring to the above classification it follows that potentially there can occur in nature one hundred types of energy transformation, which are listed schematically in the morphological box as shown.

The Morphological Box of Energy Transformations

Type of energy	E_1	E_2	E_3	E_4	E_5	E_6	E_7	E_8	E_9	E_{10}
E_1	E_1E_1	E_1E_2	E_1E_3	·	·	·	·	·	·	E_1E_{10}
E_2	E_2E_1	E_2E_2	E_2E_3	·	·	·	·	·	·	E_2E_{10}
E_3	E_3E_1	E_3E_2	E_3E_3	·	·	·	·	·	·	E_3E_{10}
E_4	·	·	·	·	·	·	·	·	·	·
E_5	·	·	·	·	·	·	·	·	·	·
E_6	·	·	·	·	·	·	·	·	·	·
E_7	·	·	·	·	·	·	·	·	·	·
E_8	·	·	·	·	·	·	·	·	·	·
E_9	·	·	·	·	·	·	·	·	·	·
E_{10}	$E_{10}E_1$	$E_{10}E_2$	$E_{10}E_3$	·	·	·	·	·	·	$E_{10}E_{10}$

For example: $E_1E_1 =$ conversion of kinetic energy into kinetic energy; $E_1E_2 =$ conversion of kinetic energy into elastic energy; $E_7E_9 =$ conversion of chemical energy into nuclear energy, and so on.

The morphological box of energy conversions has been chosen as the principal subject of discussion and analysis for two monographs to be issued by the *Society for Morphological Research*. The first one of these books is intended as a complete collection of illustrations and analyses of each of the hundred energy conversions E_iE_k by means of examples which deal respectively with phenomena in the microscopic, the macroscopic, and the cosmic world. This monograph will therefore list three hundred cases, whose descriptions and evaluation promises to become of importance both for purposes of instruction and as a stimulus to future potential inventors. The value of such a treatise would be considerably enhanced if universities were to prepare lecture courses in experimental physics, chemistry, and biology in which all of these energy conversions would be practically demonstrated. Our second monograph then will contain descriptions, drawings, and diagrams of devices and machines that make use of the various energy conversions for scientific, industrial, and medical purposes, as well as for communications, in agriculture, and so on.

A Few Highlights in the Exploration and Application of the Various Types of Energy

Except for the recognition of the existence of at least ten types of energy, the discovery that energy can never be lost is probably the most important result of modern science in this realm. According to my former colleague Professor P. S. Epstein (see his *Thermodynamics*, John Wiley & Sons, Inc., New York, 1957) the first step in recognition and correct formulation of the principle of the conservation of energy, which is also called the first integral principle of thermodynamics and which is equivalent to the statement that a perpetuum mobile of the first kind is impossible, must be credited to the Swiss universal scientist and philosopher Albrecht von Haller (1708–77). On the basis of his experimental studies in physiology Haller was the first to clearly recognize the equivalence of heat and of energy of motion. He thus knew that motion can produce heat.

The more intricate laws that describe the reverse conversion of heat into kinetic energy and into electrical energy were explored, elucidated and mathematically formulated by some of the greatest physicists of the nineteenth century. These laws constitute the essence of thermodynamics. The principal law of this important branch of physics is the second law of thermodynamics or the impossibility of a perpetuum mobile of the second kind. Because of its generality the most far-reaching conclusions can be derived from it, but among the laws of nature it is also one of the most difficult to understand and apply.

For the third and perhaps most revolutionary basic advance in modern times, the special theory of relativity, we are of course indebted to Albert Einstein (1879–1955) and in small part to the Viennese physicist Fritz Hasenoehrl (1874–1915). Both of these men visualized that energy, as we have already mentioned, can, so to speak, be stored and disguised as mass of the elementary particles of matter, or generally as the mass of any kind of matter.

For instance, light quanta of high enough frequency, and therefore of high enough energy, in reaction with atomic nuclei or in high electric fields can be transformed into pairs of positive and negative electrons or into pairs of positive and negative protons. In the reverse reactions positive and negative elementary particles can annihilate each other and generate radiation. The existence of processes that convert mass into energy has seriously altered our outlook for the future, in particular because it resulted in our success in unleashing the energy stored in some metastable atoms or rather in their nuclei. This is an achievement, however, which if mishandled threatens to annihilate the human race and much of the Earth.

The Relative Importance of the Various Conversions of Energy

The individual types of energy transformations prove to be respectively of quite different relative importance for the events in the microscopic, macroscopic and cosmic world. For instance, the direct transformation of radiation into kinetic energy plays only a minor role among our industrial uses of energy and energy generation. On the other hand this process in the cosmic world, incredibly enough, provides a probable explanation for the existence of suspected powerful "launchers of stars." Indeed, the intense radiation and enormous gas clouds being ejected from supernovae and from possible chains of supernovae at very great speeds of many thousands of kilometers per second may first push surrounding interstellar gas and dust clouds out of the way. These, once in motion, will subsequently pull stars and even groups of stars after them by their gravitational attraction and thus give rise to the so-called run-away stars and star streams. How such energy conversions, following each other in sequences of action, can also give rise to the intergalactic formations of bridges and jets between widely separated galaxies—which I first discovered thirty years ago, and of which thousands have now been located— will be discussed in a later section of this book devoted to astronomy. The most recent addition to our knowledge, of course, is that in many cases cosmic radiosources are associated with the mentioned formation indicating that the reverse process of the conversion of motion into radiation is one of the major phenomena involved.

In contradistinction to the conversion of radiation into motion, the transformation E_5E_5 of electrical energy into electrical energy does not seem to play any significant role in large-scale cosmic events. On the other hand this conversion is of the very greatest importance in the practice of power generation, inasmuch as for various purposes, current of a given intensity and frequency must be changed into a current of different intensity or frequency. In particular, the transmission of electrical energy over long distances must make use of very high voltages in order to minimize losses, while for the final applications transformers have to be installed to bring the voltages down to much lower levels. If direct currents are called for, the alternating currents must be conducted and transformed through rectifiers. Such conversions of electrical currents of one intensity and frequency into another are accomplished easily and with the highest efficiencies known in technology by the mentioned transformers and rectifiers. While these efficiencies approach the theoretically possible optima, even a scientist of universal knowledge will find it difficult to think of any events in nature in which the conversion of electrical energy into electrical energy on a large scale is of any importance, and where in addition, it proceeds with any appreciable efficiency. Perhaps such exchanges take place in some measure among the electric currents in the Earth's ionosphere or within the sunspots of the solar atmosphere.

Technical Applications of the Various Energy Transformations

These applications may be classified as follows: (a) technical applications that are of importance for industrial, commercial and agricultural purposes as well as for communication, in medicine and perhaps for recreation and play, and (b) applications in science for the purpose of constructing measuring instruments, control apparatus and auxiliary equipment of all kind.

The number of devices that operate with energy transformations on a small scale for purposes of control, for the activation or generation of the many phenomena, which are being studied by the scientists, as well as for measuring instruments and testing machines today is enormous. Their enumeration and description would require a large separate treatise, whose compilation we must leave to others. We mention here only the examples of radio and television transmitters and receivers that transform conventionally available electrical energy into electromagnetic radiations of various wavelengths. As a new development, which promises to become of immense importance, attention must be called to the so-called Masers and Lasers. These devices serve on the one hand as exceedingly precise controls in atomic clocks, in spectrographs and recorders attached to the radio telescopes, for instance. On the other hand they can generate monochromatic and well-directed parallel beams of coherent short wavelength electromagnetic radiation and of light at such enormous intensities that signals could be sent into cosmic space that an observer on the star Sirius, at a distance of about ten light years, could register with apparatus available to us, if there were such observers.

As technically important examples of other transformations of energy the following may serve: (a) the transformation of the gravitational potential energy of water stored behind power dams or barrages in rivers into kinetic energy. This is accomplished by the flow through Francis turbines when much water of low head is available. Small amounts of water of high head are directed as high velocity jets on the intricately shaped cup blades of Pelton wheels; (b) the transformation of the kinetic energy of the water turbines or wheels into electrical energy. This can be accomplished with very high efficiency through the use of electric generators connected to the shafts of the water turbines. As is well known, electric generators work on the principle of the famous law of electromagnetic induction, first discovered by the great British physicist Michael Faraday.

Of major importance are the thermal power plants that generate a large proportion of all of the mechanical and electrical energy used all over the world. These plants may conveniently be divided into two classes, which can be designated as stationary and propulsive power plants, the latter ones being engines in motion.

Among the stationary thermal power plants two general types may be distinguished depending on whether the heat generated by the combustion of the fuels is first transmitted to a neutral working fluid or the hot gases of combustion themselves are used for the activation of the engines. Examples of the first one of these two types are the steam engines and the steam turbines. In these machines the heat liberated by the combustion of the fuels is applied to evaporate water as the neutral working fluid. The vapour thus generated is then allowed to expand in a cylinder or pass through the blades of a turbine wheel and in this way to set respectively a piston or a wheel in motion.

In a reciprocating combustion engine, on the other hand, or in a gas turbine—that is in devices of the second type mentioned above—the hot combustion gases are acting directly on the pistons or on the blades of turbine wheels, as the case may be.

Among the typical propulsive power plants moving either themselves or mounted on moving vehicles, those are presently of particular importance that by means of chemical reactions generate heat that is subsequently transformed into the kinetic energy of directed gas jets. Because of the forces of reaction caused by the exhaust of these very fast jets (with velocities of two to three kilometers per second) vehicles like rockets, airplanes, torpedoes, and submarines may be propelled and either accelerated or moved at a steady speed against the resistance of the surrounding medium. As a further distinction propulsive power plants may be classified as pure medium engines or as interfacial engines; the latter are moving along the interface of two media, for instance water and air, and they make use of both media for purposes of chemical reaction and thrust augmentation.

In present-day practice the conversion of chemical energy into mechanical energy is always realized by means of an intermediary step, that is, reacting the chemical reagents first for the purpose of generating heat and hot gases, as in the example of the gas turbine mentioned above. In order to propel a rocket, for instance, fuel and oxydizer are introduced (or they may have been stored there to start with) into a thrust chamber and reacted, whereupon the hot gases generated are made to expand through a nozzle and thus form a fast exhaust jet. As a consequence of this gain of momentum of the gases in one direction, forces of reaction are set up which accelerate the rocket in the direction opposite to the jet. An isothermal or constant temperature conversion of chemical energy into mechanical energy is also possible, for instance, by using gaseous hydrogen and oxygen as the propellants, as I demonstrated in 1944, when I was director of research of the Aerojet Engineering Corporation (now Aerojet General), in Azusa, California. This conversion, however, requires a rather sophisticated handling of all operations and has not yet been used in practice, although it will have to be introduced as soon as very high energy propellants become available.

Transformation of Chemical Energy Into Chemical Energy

This type of energy conversion takes place in plants, and fortuitously in those which produce all sorts of substances necessary for man and animal to remain alive, that is foodstuffs in particular. As already mentioned, the plants make use of the raw materials available in the earth, in the water, and in the air, while the ambient heat and solar radiation supply the energy necessary for the beneficiation of these materials into high grade chemical compounds. For the time being we know of no adequate substitute for the work the plants do for us. For this reason the danger that radioactive fallout from nuclear bomb tests—which contains radioactive isotopes like carbon 14, strontium 90 and iodine 131—will contaminate our food supplies is a consequence of one of the most flagrant and irresponsible misuses of the results of fundamental scientific research, and it must be averted at all costs if man is to survive.

The direct transformation of chemical energy into electrical energy can be realized on a small scale through the generation of electrical currents in an electrochemical battery. If the current drawn off is very weak, the efficiency of this conversion is actually very high, close to 100 per cent. Curiously enough, it has not been possible so far to adapt this process for the generation of electrical power on a large scale. Actually we are here confronted with one of the old, most important, but as yet unsolved problems of science and technology, for instance the direct generation of electrical energy through the oxydation of ordinary fuels such as gasoline, kerosine and, especially, coal. Scientists have named this the problem of the *power cell*, or more appropriately of the chemical propellant flow battery. This cell is the equivalent of a continually operating electrical battery into which fuel and air are fed on one side, while the equivalent electrical current energy becomes available at the electrodes, and the reaction products are bled off at constant temperature and ambient pressure on the other side of the cell. As many of the most prominent scientists and engineers have emphasized for the last hundred years, the solution of the problem of the so-called "carbon cell" in particular is of the greatest importance. In this cell solid coal would be oxydized by the air introduced and electrical current generated directly, without the intervention of any thermal combustion in the ordinary sense.

Many of the propulsive power plants invented since 1940, such as the novel types of rockets, space ships and engines for airplanes, ocean surface boats, torpedoes, submarines and so on, will only become practical for large scale industrial, commercial, and military applications once suitable and cheap high energy propellants have been developed and become available for their operation. This applies in particular to the intricate *terrajet engines*, which I think will be indispensable if we are ever to succeed in exploring and exploiting "Inner Space," that is, the interior of the Earth. As a result of new types of propellants we can already clearly visualize methods which will enable us to launch single-stage rockets from the Earth to the Moon and actually to the most distant members of the solar system. These propellants will eventually be produced through persevering research in the fields of *high energy chemistry, fragment chemistry* (mostly the chemistry of free radicals), and *metachemistry*. Since more will be said later, I mention here only that we intend to develop successively substances of the following types: (a) compounds of boron with other light elements such as hydrogen and nitrogen, (b) chemical radicals or other fragments of molecules stabilized in bulk of macroscopic density, (c) thermodynamically pseudostable compounds, such as helium hydride *HeH*, which would in some sense be analogous to the well-known pseudostable and potentially explosive acetylene C_2H_2, again in macroscopic bulk density.

The conversion of *nuclear energy*, for instance the energy released by nuclear reactors through the fission of uranium into *mechanical energy*, need not here be further discussed. The stationary nuclear reactor plants for the production of electrical power are by now well known and have been extensively discussed both in the professional and the lay literature. The same is true for the steam turbine plants, which are being supplied the necessary steam and energy by nuclear reactors on the American submarines of the classes of the *Nautilus* and the *Sea Wolf*, as well as more recently for the power plants of some of the ocean-going surface ships.

The problem of the *continuous conversion of nuclear fusion energy* into mechanical, electrical or chemical energy remains with us as one of the most important challenges with which we must deal. A first step towards the release of energy by nuclear fusion has of course been made in the realization of the hydrogen bomb. If the analogous conversion can be achieved through the use of commonly available materials, power supplies of such unimaginable capacity will become available to us that all existing power plants would literally become antiquated from one day to the next. And more than that, the mastery of nuclear fusion processes would allow us to travel around the planetary system with the greatest of ease and would also enable us to create adequate conditions for the continuous habitation by man of the Moon, the planets and their satellites. The further breathtaking possibility also suggests itself of igniting limited areas of the Sun to nuclear fusion in such a way that the directed exhaust jets would accelerate it, by their recoil, to velocities high enough to carry it to the nearest stars, say Alpha Centauri within the total life span of fifty generations, while the Earth would be dragged along by the Sun.

As we have said, the mastery of the ignition of nuclear fusion of the most abundant light elements of the Earth's crust, such as hydrogen, boron, carbon, oxygen, magnesium, calcium, aluminum, silicon, and so on, into some of the most stable medium nuclei, such as iron, nickel, and cobalt, would not only open up a practically inexhaustible source of energy, but would also enable us to produce at will all the essential foodstuffs and construction materials from common rocks. We could then in principle dispense with agriculture and mining and keep plants and animals only for their beauty, companionship, and because of our scientific interest in the processes that govern the evolution of living matter. We might, however, never be able to reproduce all the delicacies in foods and drinks which nature furnishes us, and we would thus no doubt by common vote decide to retain many of them. On the other hand our first emigrants to the Moon and the planets would have a hard time if all of the operations necessary for their livelihood there had to be carried out without benefit of the availability of the energies and materials that can be obtained from controlled nuclear fusion reactions of common matter.

Finally, attention must be called to the fact that besides gravitation, nuclear fusion reactions in the cosmic events of the universe play perhaps the second most important role. Indeed the stars, during eons, have radiated immense amounts of energy into interstellar and intergalactic space. We believe that most of this energy has been liberated within the stars by nuclear fusion reactions and in particular through "hydrogen burning." In this process, which proceeds only at sufficiently high temperatures, protons, neutrons, and electrons are fused together so as to produce the nuclei of the heavier elements like deuterium, helium, carbon, nitrogen, and so on. As a consequence of these fusion processes amounts of energy are liberated per gram of the reagents that are billions of times greater than those obtainable per gram from the most powerful chemical reactions.

Positive Accomplishments and Tragic Blunders and Misuses

There can be no doubt that the men of research and the engineers have been extraordinarily successful in their investigations and their practical efforts to supply the human community with the necessary or desired amounts of thermal, mechanical, electrical, chemical, and nuclear energy. As I have emphasized in the first two chapters the results achieved have often been usurped by selfish, power-hungry, and criminal individuals and have been stupidly misused and wasted, thus causing all sorts of miseries and catastrophes as a consequence. By way of illustration we mention the shameful exploitation of the working man during the long and painful ascendancy of the industrial age, the irrational and exceedingly wasteful development of all means of traffic and communication, the irresponsible slaughter and maiming of millions of people through unplanned production and poorly controlled use of automobiles, pollution of the atmosphere and the water supplies, which result from the exhausts of automobiles and the careless handling of all waste products from both industrial establishments and private homes, as well as the effects of radioactive fallouts, and finally, to top it all, the murderous uses of the results of research and technology for the conduction of innumerable modern wars and revolutions.

It bears repeating that, if ever in the past any success was achieved in stemming the abuses of major scientific and technical achievements, this rare feat was almost always the result of the *cooperation of scientists, phsyicians, engineers and lawyers* who, joining hands, could exert enough pressure on the authorities or on confused and overambitious politicians to force their respective actions into reasonable channels. The same kind of cooperation, but on a planned and much more universal scale will be absolutely indispensable for all major actions now and in the near future if we are to cope successfully with the dangers we have conjured through the unleashing of atomic energy, and if we are to avoid all the various types of abuses of the scientific and technical gains mentioned.

Third Application of the Method of the Morphological Box: The Totality of Interrelations in the Abstract World; The Morphology of Justice in the Space Age

Our subject, which in this age of artificial Earth satellites, space sondes, manned space capsules, and coming space ships is of particularly urgent interest, may be viewed conveniently from three different angles.

First it is obvious that the problem of justice in the space age is of immense complexity. Exactly for this reason it is eminently suited to be subjected to the morphological approach the value of which in the review and analysis of intricate interrelations, can thus be convincingly demonstrated. As I have explained in the earlier chapters, morphological research concerns itself in the first place with the elucidation and development of the *fundamentals of thought and procedure* and only in the second place with the teaching of specific techniques and the construction of temples of learning, which are the activities pursued presently by the representatives of the conventional disciplines in science and education.

In the *second place* I shall attempt to show that the morphological approach, among all available modes of inquiry, is particularly appropriate and perhaps the most powerful possible when applied to the field of justice, that is to the formulation of the law and to the means of its enforcement. Parenthetically, it is interesting to note that it was precisely the lawyers and judges who were among the first to recognize the significance and make use of morphological methods. As a consequence an international body among them invited me to give the inaugural address on this topic at the meeting on October 3, 1961, in Washington, D.C., of the International Astronautical Federation.

Third I shall try to illustrate how one readily succeeds in applying the morphological approach in a satisfactory manner to the problems of justice in the space age. In this connection the foundations of an Institute of Space Law within the International Astronautical Federation, whose avowed purpose it is to help formulate a universally acceptable code of law for outer space, and eventually for inner space, will be hailed by all people of good will as an important step forward, since it helps us to focus our attention on an entirely new set of circumstances, which have emerged recently and must be dealt with speedily and appropriately. The representatives of the Institute of Space Law have justifiably emphasized the necessity that, in addition to scientific and technical questions, human problems of the greatest importance must be solved. Otherwise we are in danger of blundering into the space age as stupidly and irresponsibly as we have blundered into most of the evolutionary events in the past.

Although the specialists have solved innumerable important problems of a more or less limited scope in all branches of human endeavor, the *integration* of the knowledge and experiences gained for the purpose of the full development of all creative forces in man has not yet reached the same high level. This is in part due to the facts that one has unduly overestimated the role the specialists are capable of playing in the solution of general human problems and the task of a comprehensive integration and application of all knowledge has been sadly neglected. The morphological approach has been specifically conceived with this universal goal in mind, and it has been developed and implemented accordingly during the past three decades.

In my opinion it is the morphologist's unbiased and comprehensive way of seeing things that promises to contribute the most *to the integral treatment of complex problems.* For this reason it would be difficult to think of any discipline that intrinsically has closer bonds to the morphological methods of thought than jurisprudence. Indeed, for a true understanding of the world of law and for the correct application of its tenets, strict unbias is the first and absolutely indispensable prerequisite. Furthermore, lawyers and judges must be imaginative enough to visualize correctly entire complexes of material configurations, physico-chemical phenomena and intricate concepts, and they must be able to do so to a far greater extent than almost any other professional. The value of these potential capabilities becomes evident particularly in some of those sensational cases in which the courts must decide as to who has committed a murder, and the decision must be made, according to the law, regardless of the fact that sometimes only indirect and insufficient clues are available. Everyone knows of the numerous tragic cases throughout the history of man in which innocents were hanged because of the stupidity or the prejudices of the jurors or the judge, and the law thus became the murderer itself.

Unbias and an all-embracing imaginative mind are indispensable whenever new laws and directives for their enforcement must be formulated. The same requirements apply if the morphological approach is to be followed. The jurist of the space age must therefore try to become a morphologist to as high a degree as possible, and as such he will then in addition team up with those scientists, physicians, and engineers who are the most intimately acquainted with the facts of the world.

The reader may at this point puzzle over the question of what the author, as an outsider to jurisprudence, thinks he can contribute to the formulation of a code of law for the Space Age. To propose an analogous question, he might also inquire what a morphologist would be able to suggest for the construction of a suitable shorthand system for the Chinese language although not actually acquainted with this language.

But even in this extreme case the morphologist is not lost. On the contrary he will immediately point out that every language makes use of the same universal structural characters, for instance sounds, words, phrases, and definite sequences of phrases, and these are intended to describe events, opinions, actions, vocations, avocations, and so on, which may often be of a quite stereotyped character. He will further emphasize that the formalism that must be adopted for the recording of these various characteristics can be achieved through certain subjective and objective means such as the eyes, touch, and the other senses, as well as with the aid of one's own hands and legs, or those of others, and with assistance of various mechanical devices. Furthermore, if one chooses, for example, to write with a pencil, he may use dots, dashes, straight and curved lines, shaded strongly or weakly, which are continuously drawn or dashed, and if grid lines are available on the writing paper, all symbols may be placed on, below or above the printed lines. Furthermore short, medium, and large spacing can be chosen between the symbols to express different meanings, and one may write from the left to the right or vice versa. All of these features are available for the construction of a shorthand system, regardless of what language is to be recorded. Through this visualization of the totality of all the means of recording, the morphologist can materially assist any expert linguist in the development of a shorthand system for his respective language. Likewise, a morphologist who is not a professional jurist may render important services in the formulation of a code of law for the Space Age, if he is given the opportunity to cooperate with men of legal training and technical professionals who possess sufficient knowledge about all relevant technical facts. I hope that this will answer the question about why I and others who are nonprofessionals in matters of jurisprudence participate actively in the work of the legal scientific committee of the International Academy of Astronautics. In the following I shall describe plans and some of the work I hope this very competent international group will do so that we shall not blunder head over heels into the Space Age.

A STUDY OF THE MORPHOLOGY OF JUSTICE IN THE SPACE AGE

This study can be conducted in two stages, the first of which is concerned with a "holding action," while the second will be devoted to planning and developments of long duration.

The Holding Action

The necessity of an effective holding action has been recognized from the beginning by the members of the Institute of Space Law and has been promoted especially convincingly and effectively by my old friend Andrew Haley in Washington, D.C. Mr. Haley, whose untimely death in 1966 has left us to do the work without his superior knowledge and vision in these matters, was one of the first to insist that all agencies launching any kinds of missiles around the Earth or into interplanetary space should be asked to abstain from such projects unless they can guarantee that they can adequately control the course of their missiles. Otherwise an ever-increasing number of these bodies traveling criss-cross through space might eventually cause us troubles of all kinds. For example, Haley has pointed out that transmitters on space sondes which are activated by solar batteries may get lost in interplanetary space and stay "alive" for a long time. If powerful enough they would thus interfere with future regular channels of radio communication and with the observations of the radio-astronomers.

Another most serious problem would arise if one of the countries concerned with the development of nuclear energy decides to dispose of the resulting radioactive waste products by dumping them into interplanetary space. As a consequence of such procedures we would eventually be confronted not only with a radioactive contamination of our atmosphere and of all the bodies on the surface of the Earth, but also possibly with a catastrophic dispersion of radioactive products through other parts of the solar system.

In connection with the mentioned problems a few most disturbing thoughts come to my mind. From initial tests I have conducted I am convinced that with relatively simple means macroscopic particles, first perhaps of colloidal size, can be accelerated to velocities of up to 1,000 kilometers per second. On impact of such particles with massive solid or liquid bodies, nuclear fusion will be ignited, or in the case of elements heavier than iron, fission of some of the respective nuclei will result. Once this can be accomplished, however, the danger arises that, as a consequence of careless experimentation, the whole Earth or vital parts of it, such as the oceans, might be exploded. In order to bring these possibilities and risks forcibly and drastically to the attention of the public and the many unimaginative and calcified professionals, I have suggested many years ago that we initiate, whenever feasible, an integral nuclear fusion reaction on one of the smaller asteroids or planetoids, that is on one of those tiny members of the solar system that travel mostly on orbits concentrated between Mars and Jupiter. Since no lone individual by himself can be certain, however, to think of all and evaluate all of the consequences of such an undertaking, I shall try to seize every occasion to discuss the various aspects and implications of such a drastic demonstration of impending events with competent and responsible colleagues. Such exchanges of opinion will form a major contribution to the holding action that must precede the final planning and the practical realization of our march into space.

Every reasonable man will furthermore be aghast at the prospect that we might propogate our differences and quarrels on Earth to other parts of the Solar System, and that the stupidity of man will serve as the guiding spirit for our future actions in space.

As a first step in our crusade for reason, my colleagues of the International Academy of Astronautics and I appeal to all men of good will to cooperate and work towards an agreement concerning an effective holding action for the preservation of all irreplaceable values in outer space. Only in this way can we prevent irresponsible and stupid bunglers, blunderers, wastrels, and outright criminals from destroying much that should be preserved for the construction of a unified and stabilized world.

We now proceed to elaborate a few of the essential morphological aspects of justice in the space age.

The Concept of Law

The practical application of the morphological approach involves the following steps: (a) An exact description of the goals which are to be accomplished and all the basic concepts involved; (b) The enumeration of all the possible avenues that might lead us to the desired goals; (c) The unbiased evaluation of all the conceivable modes of action considered under (b); (d) The selection and practical application of the most adequate solutions.

Definitions

If we intend to follow the plans indicated above, we first must clearly formulate what we mean by *law* and *justice*. In a dictionary we find *law* defined as "a rule of conduct or action established by custom or laid down and enforced by a governing authority," and it says *justice* is "the administration of what is just." I am inclined to claim that no such nebulous definition will satisfy any hard-boiled morphologist, or for that matter, help us much with the establishment of a satisfactory code of law for the Space Age. Still worse, the definitions of law and justice given in different languages are quite different, so many discussions between men of good will and a thorough knowledge of several languages by each one of the prospective conferees will be necessary as a preliminary to the formulation of justice in the Space Age. As to the two definitions given above, the first is weak, since it refers to conduct only as established by custom and not as boldly visualized for the future. Indeed, if we had to wait for the code of law for space to be established by custom, all would be lost. Such a code must be decided upon, long in advance, by men of vision and universal knowledge about the things that are to come. And the second definition falls short of what we need because it defines the concept of *justice* inadequately by the respective adjective *just*, which essentially refers only to the mutual relations among men. The additional relations of man to the universe as a whole however, require that our code of law also consider the aspects of justice towards this universe, which means that all actions must be compatible and must be synchronized with the laws of nature so that man and his surroundings will progress in unison and develop in harmony, avoiding catastrophic events either to man or nature.

Using the morphological approach, it is best to start with the simplest elements, no matter how insignificant and unimportant these might appear to be. We therefore discuss first the following basic morphological definitions:

LAW AND THE ADMINISTRATION OF JUSTICE

I suggest the following formalistic definitions, which subsequently must be filled with the proper concrete contents. The law circumscribes a certain definite code of conduct. Justice is compliance with this adopted code of conduct.

An individual who acts in accordance with the rules of the adopted code acts justly; he is a just individual. If his actions deviate from the adopted code, he acts unjustly, he is an unjust individual. (To those who might violently object that such codes might be outrageously unjust as seen by other people, or if that were possible, *sub speciae eternitatis*, the answer is that they may well be correct, but we are not in the beginning concerned with valuations, but only with the strictness and the unambiguity of the definitions of terms and concepts.)

To take a trivial case: Certain rules have been adopted for playing chess. One rule is that no player should ever put a piece exactly on the dividing line between a black and a white square so that his opponent does not know on which square the piece stands.

As to the definition of the administration of justice it must be decided whether or not there should be any consequences, that is if any punishment should be meted out to those who act unjustly and vice versa, and whether there might be any gratuities for those who act justly.

Taking the case of our chess player, the administrator of justice would, for instance, disqualify the unjust player from participation in the current competition, or even disqualify him from participation in any further competitions, and so on.

Having adopted these definitions of justice and of administration of justice, the morphologist is confronted with the obvious task of establishing the morphological boxes or parametric arrays of, *first*, the basic possible types of codes of conduct and, *second*, the basic possible types of punishments and bonuses.

The Morphological Box of Possible Codes of Conduct

It will naturally be the task of a competent working group of experts in many fields and of universal outlook to establish a suitable morphological box of all possible major types of conduct. Just what such a box should look like in principle is demonstrated by the following oversimplified array.

Morphological Box of Codes of Conduct

Parameters	Components of the Parameters		
P_1 Conceptual character	P_{11} Dictatorial	P_{12} Mutual Consent	P_{13} Absolutely Objective
P_2 Qualitative character of the standard	P_{21} Body animate, inanimate	P_{22} Phenomenon	P_{23} Concept
P_3 Consequences of deviations from the code	P_{31} None	P_{32} Destructive	P_{33} Constructive

Our morphological box contains twenty-seven types of codes of conduct which are designated by the matrices $[P_{1r}, P_{2s}, P_{3t}]$ where r, s, and t all may assume the values 1, 2, and 3.

Example 1: The United States of America attempts to force its democratic way of life, as they understand it, upon the people of some small nation, and they are subsequently reprimanded for this action by the General Assembly of the United Nations. This case would be formally described by the matrix $[P_{11}, P_{23}, P_{32}]$, because the intended action was dictatorial in character (P_{11}), it was undertaken for the purpose of having the little nation in question recognize and appreciate the value of a certain concept ($P_{23} =$

concept of American democracy) and finally the action was condemned (P_{32} = punished).

Example 2: A group of engineers, after studying the morphological box of all possible bridge constructions, chooses the one that is best for making possible the crossing of a certain river at or near a prescribed location and, after a successful and economically most advantageous construction, is honoured for this achievement by some institution, for instance the National Academy of Applied Sciences of their respective country. Such a project could be described by the matrix $[P_{13}, P_{21}, P_{33}]$, because the engineers have proceeded with the greatest objectivity (P_{13}), the standard involved was the construction of a material (inanimate) object (P_{21}), and the achievement was honored because of its positive constructive value (P_{33}).

The next step in the morphological analysis consists in evaluating the various codes of conduct in the light of some set values concerning the problem of justice in the space age. For instance, if we are only interested in a type of justice that will avoid major conflicts both among men and between men and nature, all codes designated as P_{11}, P_{2s}, P_{3t}, that is all those for which $r = 1$, are to be ruled out. There would then remain only six principal codes of conduct. Among these the codes that involve mutual consent are of course well known to all jurists, and in fact to all men, since they have been discussed for thousands of years. There has been, however, far too little emphasis on the cases $[P_{13}, P_{2s}, P_{3t}]$ that are based on the universal recognition of some intrinsically valid code of conduct and might, therefore be automatically acceptable to all. Now these are the types of conduct that have been claimed as universally valid, that is God-given, by many of the religions. Although several of these religions almost automatically attracted adherents and believers by the hundreds of millions, the fact that the whole of humanity was never involved indicates some fatal lack of universality. It is therefore of the utmost interest to find out if such universal validity exists for any conceivable code of conduct at all. It is my personal conviction that a desirable goal of this type does exist, and that it has its origin in an elementary fact, which has hitherto been ignored, or which at best has only been partly recognized. I am referring to the fact that every individual is a genius in the sense that he is incomparable, irreplaceable, and capable of mental and physical performances that cannot be equaled by any other individual. For the present I must leave the reader with these statements. He will realize, however, that if my assertions are valid, we would have found an intrinsic code of conduct that should ultimately be universally acceptable and would serve admirably for the institution of justice in the Space Age as well as for the administration of justice.

My outlook on the matter under consideration therefore is as follows:

1. Persuade all individuals of the basic fact that everyone is a genius in the sense described above.

2. Develop criteria to find out in each case where the genius of any given individual lies and consider the analogous problem, the specific characteristics of whole peoples.

3. Develop methods of education, communication, and construction that will help every individual to realize his genius, and take care that the interrelations among the various nations make the fullest use of the respective characteristic potentialities of their peoples.

4. Adopt the goals stated under 3 for the formulations of a code of law and justice for the Space Age.

5. Work out the administration of justice on the basis of a morphological analysis of the ideas stated above.

As to the significance of the parameters P_2 and P_3 it may be said that P_{21}, for example, means that according to some adopted code of conduct only certain types of bodies could be projected into space, while others would be prohibited. For instance, all launching of radioactive waste into space would be forbidden. Likewise, only certain types of physico-chemical actions (P_{22}) would be permitted, while others would not be tolerated. Finally, as an example of P_{23} we might mention the concept of the sovereignty over extraterrestrial bodies. Possible alternatives are that this sovereignty would be left to whoever comes first, or that some collective sovereignty might be decided upon, as in the case of Antarctica.

The meaning of the parameter P_3 is essentially self-evident, inasmuch as certain choices of the parameters P_1 and P_2 will lead to different types of consequences—destructive, constructive, or neutral.

Recommendations

As a result of the considerations presented above, the following plans for future action suggest themselves:

(a) Formulate an appropriate holding action, which concerns all of the legal aspects of man's march into space. Actually such actions are already underway but they would be strengthened through systematic use of the morphological approach.

(b) Formulate the basic aspects of the morphology of justice in the Space Age and attempt to achieve a united front of all agencies involved.

(c) Tasks (a) and (b) can be handled in many ways. It is my personal conviction, however, that they can be dealt with most efficiently only through use of the morphological approach.

(d) The aid of many specialists will have to be mobilized for the supply of the necessary pegs of scientific, technical, legal, and human knowledge. Likewise, to achieve a united front, the support of the specialists as well as of existing professional organizations must be sought. I would like to mention the International Astronomical Union (IAU), whose members and associated observatories and academic institutions in the various countries possess by far the greatest knowledge of what goes on in outer space and what operations, observations and experiments man will be able to perform out there.

Fortunately the International Astronautical Federation (IAF) also clearly recognizes the necessity of proper planning of man's march into space. As far as the necessity for a holding action is concerned, the IAU is in complete accord with the efforts of the members of the International Institute of Space Law, and I think, with the views which I have expressed. In fact, at the General Assembly in Berkeley, California, in September, 1961, the IAU expressed concern and unanimously adopted a resolution to be sent as a warning to the government of the United States concerning the undesirability of the so-called project Westford (bundles of fine copper needles to be launched into an orbit around the Earth for purposes of testing reflection of radio waves).

My final suggestion, made at the meeting of the IAF in Washington, D.C., in October, 1961, therefore, was that international groups be formed for the morphological study of the problems of justice in the Space Age, and such groups base their work on all the factual and projected knowledge that can be supplied by all qualified professional sources.

Progress since that memorable meeting, in Washington, D.C., in 1961 has been unexpectedly rapid and most satisfying indeed. The efforts of the Institute of Space Law, the International Academy of Astronautics and many interested groups and individuals bore fruit inasmuch as the basic suggestions made were taken up by responsible members of various governments, about twenty-eight of which, including Russia and the United States of America sent their representatives to Geneva in the summer of 1966 to deliberate on the formulation of a preliminary space treaty. Amazingly enough a number of the most important clauses were readily agreed upon by the envoys present, and a treaty was formulated which is now up for ratification by the parliaments of the various nations. In the United States this treaty has been unanimously approved by the Senate Foreign Relations Committee and will come up for ratification in April (1967).* Some of the fundamental principles included in the treaty are:

---

* As I am writing these additions to the English edition of my present book the news has just been released (end of April, 1967) that by a vote of 88 to o the United States Senate has approved the "Treaty for Outer Space."

There is, however, one ominous clause included in the treaty which states that on a one-year notice any one of the signatories may renounce adhesion to the treaty. This means that mutual trust is still drastically on trial and all men of good will must relax no efforts to strengthen this trust. As it always was and always will remain, eternal vigilance is the price we must pay for a free world.

No nation can claim sovereignty to outer space, to the Moon or to other celestial bodies.

All nations have the right to conduct space activities.

No one may use outer space or celestial bodies to begin a war.

The rules of the United Nations charter apply to space activities.

No country may station in space or orbit around the Earth nuclear or other weapons of mass destruction.

No country may install such weapons on a celestial body.

No nation may establish military bases, installations, or fortifications on a celestial body. Nor may any weapon be tested or military maneuvers be conducted there. The right to visit another country's installations and space vehicles on a celestial body is guaranteed.

Astronauts are envoys of mankind. If an astronaut lands on another country's soil he must be returned safely, promptly and unconditionally.

Space activities and their results are to be reported for the benefit of all.

5

The Morphological Methods III:
The Method of Negation
and Construction

Generalities

In its endeavour to view the world in the proper perspective, that is, to recognize the true image of the world and add constructive new features to it, morphological research searches continually for new methods and procedures, which will enable us without fail to make ever new discoveries and inventions. One of these methods owes its development and perfection to the profound conviction that dogmas and the impeding influence of half truths and conventional or dictatorial restrictions stand in the way of constructive progress. Such dogmas, therefore, must be negated at all cost. But that is not sufficient. The insights gained as a result of any negation must immediately be made use of for purposes of sound construction. Heeding this advice and following up the well-reasoned negation of apparent truths and some of the so-called absolute facts with the constructive use of the vistas that thus open themselves, we may be certain to succeed not only in making sporadic discoveries and inventions but actually whole groups and entire classes of them.

In pure mathematics the method of negation and construction is well known. Perhaps the most widely quoted and most famous example is the development of the so-called Non-Euclidean geometry by N. I. Lobachevski (1793–1856) and J. Bolyai (1802–60). Euclid (about 300 B.C.) had constructed his wonderful system of plane geometry on the basis of certain axioms and postulates, which he considered as a priori truths and self-evident. Among these axioms the fifth is perhaps the best known and most striking. It says that through any point P which is not located on the straight line s_0 there is but one straight line s which lies in the plane through s_0 and P and does not intersect s_0. This straight line s is called a parallel to s_0. Those among my readers who since their school days have forgotten about the properties of parallels may pull out a flat piece of paper and a pencil and convince themselves again about there being only one parallel to s_0 through a point P off from it.

The three-dimensional space that can be constructed on the basis of Euclid's axioms is infinite and is often called a flat space. The sum of the angles in every flat triangle bounded by straight lines is equal to 180°, or equal to π in the mathematician's way of measuring angles by so-called radians; and the circumference of a flat circle of the radius r is equal to $2\pi r$. As late as the end of the eighteenth century the great German philosopher Immanuel Kant (1724–1804) thought of having demonstrated in his *Kritik der Reinen Vernunft* that Euclidean space is the only possible, absolute, and a priori given space. Shortly after Kant died, Lobachevski and Bolyai proved independently that, as a consequence of denying the absolute truth value of Euclid's fifth axiom and by completely disregarding it, an entirely new Non-Euclidean geometry could be conceived and structurally developed, in which the sum of the three angles in a triangle bounded by straight lines is smaller than 180° and the circumference of a flat circle is greater than $2\pi r$. This first breakthrough into new territories of geometrical concepts was vastly generalized by B. Riemann (1826–66), F. Klein (1849–1925), and other great mathematicians of the nineteenth century, who achieved some of those most fundamental results, which later on proved to be of the greatest importance for the development of the general theory of relativity, and without which the tremendous progress of modern physics and astronomy would have been impossible.

Stangely enough the method of negation and subsequent construction has never been systematically used for the enrichment of our store of knowledge in physics, astronomy, chemistry, biology, in the humanities and technology, nor has it had any serious applications in general human affairs. Only quite recently have the morphologists begun to avail themselves of this most powerful tool of thought and procedure in all fields of human endeavour. How the morphological approach effectively makes use of the method or negation and construction may be illustrated by the following three classes of examples: (a) the invention, fabrication and the uses of certain entirely new types of materials; (b) the systematic discovery of new phenomena and the formulation of new laws of nature; (c) the elucidation of certain complexes of concepts and of abstract relationships.

First Application of the Method of Negation and Construction: The Invention of New Types of Detonating Substances (Coruscatives = Heat Detonators)

We first consider the case of some distinct material or substance S, which has the properties p_1, p_2, p_3 . . . p_z, and we inquire if new types of substances S' are conceivable and producible, which lack one or more of these propertics. Since unbias and disregard of any prevaluations are two of the major requirements of morphological research, we are not interested at all, to start with, whether or not our procedure will yield results of any practical value. We shall inquire only much later on if the newly invented and fabricated substances S' (if there are any) can be used for applications for which the original substances were unfit. For instance, all solid bodies are more or less elastic (elasticity = property p_1). If, however, we subject any solid body to sufficiently powerful stresses it will be permanently deformed and ultimately break (possibility of rupture = property p_2). Considering for simplicity only these two properties p_1 and p_2 of the solid bodies, the morphologist by way of negation will ask if one or the other of these properties can be eliminated. Following up his negation with construction, he will inquire if substances S' and S'' are thinkable, which respectively have the following distinctive qualities. Devices built of materials of type S', which do not possess the property p_1, will break or rupture when sufficiently stressed, but they will not be deformed in any way by stresses smaller than the destructive yield and breaking stresses. On the other hand, bodies fabricated from materials of type S'', which do not possess the property p_2, will never rupture or break, that is, they are infinitely elastic. It is obvious that materials with remarkable mechanical characteristics, such as those of S' and S'', would be of immense value in all fields of human technology. In reality it will not be possible to produce the ideal solids of this type because the properties of the atoms themselves impose certain restrictions on those of matter in bulk. Ideal solids, however, will eventually be approximated to a much larger degree than that of which we are capable today. Here, then, lies a vast field of solid body physics and chemistry, which may be profitably explored by future generations of morphologists. Parenthetically, it should be remarked that, with the advent of the modern chemistry of plastics, substances have already been produced, which although not reversibly elastic, can be stretched enormously without being ruptured.

In the following I shall describe an interesting analogous problem, which I have been able to solve relatively speedily through the invention of what I have proposed to call coruscatives or heat detonators, and for which the United States Patent Office on June 2, 1964, granted me U.S. Patent Number 3 135 205 (Coruscative Ballistic Device). Starting again from the consideration of certain well-known substances of a given class S, we first clearly define their essential properties p_1, p_2, p_3 . . . p_z, and we inquire if, through the elimination of one of these properties, we might not succeed in producing entirely new substances, possibly with so far unavailable characteristics.

We choose the ordinary liquid or solid chemical explosives as our initial substances S. In passing, it should be pointed out that, as far as I can find out, no concise definition of an explosive is given anywhere in the scientific or technical literature. As I have repeatedly stressed, such definitions are absolutely indispensable, if one wishes to pursue morphological research with the assurance of optimum probability of success. In our case there are at least three properties characteristic for the substances of the class S. These are p_1: A chemical explosive, after proper ignition is transformed into a number of different reaction products and a certain amount of energy is thereby set free, which can be used for the production of useful mechanical and electrical power. Furthermore, p_2: The transition from the original explosive to the reaction products can be and is in general a fast one in the exact sense that a detonation wave propagates itself from one point of the explosive to other points with a velocity V_d, which is of the order of magnitude or greater than the velocity of sound V_s in the original solid or liquid body. And finally p_3: The material originally concentrated in the bulk explosive expands violently (or explodes) as a consequence of the proper ignition, whereby a part of the reaction products or possibly all of them are liberated as gases.

In connection with explosive substances S of the type described the question therefore arises whether other chemical substances S' are conceivable that possess only the properties p_1 and p_2, but not the characteristic p_3. A solid or liquid body of the class S' would thus be detonable and release heat as a consequence of its transformation into one or a number of different reaction products, and these would be hot, but they would not fly apart, that is they would remain in the liquid or solid phases.

Until recently materials of type S' were quite unknown. For this reason there was also no name available for them. Searching around for a proper word, I found the expression *coruscation*, which means a flash of light. In analogy to *explosives* the introduction into the English language of a new term *coruscatives* therefore seemed appropriate for the purpose of characterizing the potential heat detonators, which I had conceived theoretically and had subsequently produced. This designation was also accepted by the United States Patent Office. Leafing through some Latin dictionaries, I found much later that my choice had been a particularly fortunate one, inasmuch as the Latin *coruscare* not only means *to sparkle* and *to flash* but also *to oscillate or move quickly,* so that this word describes both of the potential properties p_1 and p_2 of a coruscative, namely that of producing a flash of light (and heat) as well as that of doing it very fast.

Originally I was in need of coruscatives for the fabrication of solid, usually conical inserts for shaped charges, as they are commonly used in military weaponry for the piercing of tanks and other armour (see Fig. 26).

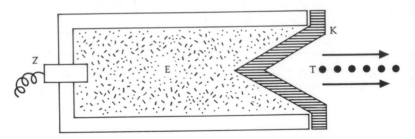

Fig. 26. Shaped charge composed of explosive E *packed within a metal cylinder, conical insert* K, *and igniter* Z.

Upon firing of the blasting cap Z the explosive E is ignited and a detonation wave propagates itself towards the conical metal or glass insert, which collapses and is ejected as a jet of small particles T along the axis of symmetry of the shaped charge. These particles, when passing through the air, become highly heated and very luminous, because of the enormous frictional forces, with the result that they lose their initial kinetic energy very quickly and generally do not travel more than a few hundred meters. For my purposes, however, I needed fast particles, which had to be launched into a vacuum and would appear very bright from the beginning. This can be achieved if one uses a coruscative for the construction of the conical insert K. The mechanical stresses set up in this insert, as a result of its collapse forced by the impinging detonation wave, are so great that the coruscative is ignited and the energy released within the ejected reacting particles themselves heats them up to a high temperature and renders them self-luminous. On October 16, 1957, we actually succeeded for the first time in the history of man in launching into interplanetary space a very hot and luminous particle of this type, consisting of titanium carbide and aluminum oxide (as the reaction products of the coruscative), from an Aerobee rocket at Alamogordo, New Mexico, from a height of eighty kilometers as the first man-made object free from the gravitational pull of the Earth, with an initial speed of fifteen kilometers per second.

As a first discovery in the search for coruscatives I found that there actually exist certain single crystals, which in the language of physical chemistry, are thermodynamically pseudostable and can be detonated with the result that they are transformed into another so-called allotropic modification, as a consequence of which transformation, more or less heat is liberated. Among the chemical elements themselves, allotropic modifications of this type occur, for instance, in the case of antimony. As a possible potential curiosity one might also consider the case of the element carbon, which in the crystalline form may exist either as graphite or as diamond. Since crystalline graphite represents the lowest free energy (or rather free enthalpy) state of carbon, it should in principle be possible to transform diamond, which corresponds to a higher energy state of this element, detonatively into graphite. Probably no one who is in possession of his good senses would think of performing such an experiment, with the exception perhaps of an incurable morphologist who is bent on investigating all the basic phenomena of nature. A professional morphologist, however, would not stop at transforming diamond into graphite. To further satisfy his scientific curiosity, he would in addition ponder the question, whether or not, after all, the more stable graphite cannot also somehow be transformed detonatively into the pseudostable diamond. It is clear, of course that this can only be done if a sufficient amount of energy is supplied from the outside, and one therefore must start with a sufficiently hot graphite crystal, or at the proper moment of the transition, one must for instance intensively irradiate the crystal. By some such procedure it should in principle be actually possible to produce diamonds from graphite crystals.

In this context it should be emphasized again that according to the teachings and the positive experiences already gathered through the use of the morphological approach *everything is possible* and everything is worth trying, if impossibility cannot be proved on the basis of the fundamental principles of physics, chemistry, and biology, and if the limitations of the human mind and body do not call for an absolute halt. It is important, but also extremely difficult to stay aware at all times of this simple guiding directive and this positive belief, if one does not wish to miss the most promising opportunities for making discoveries and inventions and especially for retrieving those which we know to have been negligently by-passed or disregarded by generations of our predecessors.

To return to our subject, the ideal coruscative would perhaps be a mixed crystal composed of various atoms or molecules, which as a whole would represent a highly energetic, thermodynamically pseudostable, but dynamically stable body, and which, on proper ignition, could transform itself detonatively with liberation of the greatest possible heat into a liquid or possibly into another solid body of a different chemical structure. Unfortunately I have not succeeded in the little spare time I have had available for the purpose in growing crystals of this type. On the other hand my friend Mr. J. Cuneo who is the secretary and legal counselor of our Society for Morphological Research, and I have managed to produce some useful coruscatives by thoroughly mixing powders and other finely subdivided aggregates, such as fibers and thin lamellae of certain chemical elements and chemical compounds and by compacting them carefully under high pressure. Our friends among the professional chemists doubted at first if, in such compacted powders, chemical reactions could be ignited detonatively. This actually proved possible with a series of combinations, for instance with powders of titanium and carbon mixed in the right proportions.* These mixtures react according to the equation Ti + C = TiC and release heat very fast without, however, exploding. The heat of reaction liberated through the combination of Ti and C amounts to 6.6 kilocalories per cubic centimeter, which is about three times as high as that obtained per cubic centimeter of the most energetic among the commonly used explosives. Another powder, which on ignition releases a great amount of heat and upon reaction remains liquid, is the world famous thermit consisting of finely divided aluminium and iron oxide. In the reaction $Fe_2O_3 + 2Al = 2Fe + Al_2O_3$ a heat of 3.6 kcal/cc is liberated. Thermit was one of the greatest technical inventions at the beginning of this century. It made possible the welding on location of broken drive shafts on even the largest ocean liners, of steel tanks of all sorts, of rails for streetcars and railroads and so on. It should be possible in principle to compress thermit powder and produce a solid coruscative; for unknown reasons, however, this has not so far proved possible, at least not through the use of commercially available materials.

As it always happens when a basic invention has been made, the further development of the idea of coruscatives led to applications of all sorts, which are more important than their use for the production and launching of ultrafast self-luminous meteors. These additional applications owe their importance to the following circumstances: First, chemical coruscatives can generate per unit volume as much as four times the heat obtainable from the best common explosives. Also, they are in themselves quite harmless and can at any time before use be admixed with ordinary explosives for the purpose of increasing their blasting power. Second, the reaction products of coruscatives act not only mechanically on the bodies into which they are being projected at

---

* Our results on the speed of propagation of the chemical reactions in coruscative were later confirmed by the United States Army Engineer Research and Development Laboratories, Fort Belvoir, Virginia, in *Technical Report* 1743-TR, March 14, 1963.

high speeds, but they also *react* thermally and especially chemically with these bodies. Since their composition can be varied widely, they may be used either as oxydizers or chemical reducers, and they therefore can be properly composed so as to react chemically with any given target. Because of this possibility of fast chemical reactions with the targets the following two important applications suggest themselves: A projectile which has been fabricated from an overoxydized coruscative, for instance, may be fired on a target that contains any kind of a fuel and that upon impact will be oxydized explosively by the very hot oxydizing agent released as a reaction product of the coruscative. In addition to military applications such projectiles could be used for the reactivation of clogged oil wells. Jets of overoxydized particles from shaped charges mounted within the drill pipes could be shot laterally at any depth into the oil soaked lime and sandstone formations. On penetration they would burn some of the oil and thus generate combustion gases at enormous pressures, which would start the remaining oil moving. The same result can be achieved today only by very expensive and cumbersome means, for instance by opening cracks in the rocks or between the strata through artificially applied enormous hydrostatic pressure. Furthermore, the possibility suggests itself that in inaccessible deserts, in mountainous regions, or on the bottoms of the oceans, where it has so far proved economically unprofitable to transport and install heavy and clumsy conventional drilling rigs, soundings for potential oil fields and even actual production drilling could be accomplished by relatively simple and more easily transportable devices. And as to still greater versatility: If the coruscatives are composed so as to release chemical reducing agents, for instance by means of excess additions of alkali or earth alkali metals such as lithium and magnesium, boron, or aluminium, these elements will be ejected as very hot liquids (or melts), and when shot into water or ice, will release gaseous hydrogen under explosive pressures. Such reactions of coruscative jets or projectiles are literally capable of hundreds of applications, among them the shattering of wet rocks on the surface of the Earth or in mines and in various types of drill holes; they can furthermore be applied for the production of short-duration large thrust forces as they are needed for the maneuvering of ships in tight places, for salvage operations under water and rescue missions of all kinds. Here also ideal uses for ice breakers and the surfacing of submarines through layers of ice suggest themselves. Finally, all sorts of sophisticated weapons may be constructed, an activity I do not wish to have considered as being of primary importance, except as a precaution for the continually recurring eventuality that power-hungry individuals and nations are bent on subduing or killing the rest of us.

And finally, to return once more to the almost unlimited potentialities of coruscatives, we must call attention to one of those earth-shaking possibilities, which every morphologist will eventually come to visualize in any field of human endeavour if he remains true to his characteristic method of total field coverage and if he uncompromisingly pursues the morphological approach to the extreme of the extremes. One of the most important and technically valuable, but also one of the most dangerous of all of the extremes would be the discovery of simple methods of nuclear fusion ignition in abundant materials such as granite and other common rocks, as a consequence of which their constituent light weight elements hydrogen, boron, carbon, oxygen, calcium, silicon, magnesium, and aluminum would be converted into iron. In these fusion reactions unimaginable amounts of energy would be released, which per gram of initial material reacted are comparable to those liberated per gram by the nuclear fission reactions in atomic bombs.

Actually, during the past two decades the scientists of many nations have worked arduously to find initiators for this type of nuclear fusion, and they have in particular expended enormous sums of money attempting to achieve success by means of the so-called plasma physics, a field of investigation upon which I shall not here dwell any further, since it has been amply discussed not only in the professional literature but also in innumerable semipopular and popular magazines and newspapers. In spite of the prodigious efforts of some of the most competent experimental physicists, the outlook for achieving nuclear fusion reactions at acceptable efficiencies within magnetically restricted plasmas of electrically positive and negative ions or oppositely charged elementary particles appears dim so far, not to mention cheaply producing unlimited amounts of useful energy in this manner. Under the circumstances it is of importance that the morphological approach be mobilized for the purpose of first reviewing *all* of the possibilities for the initiation of nuclear fusion reactions. This is particularly to be recommended, since as I have mentioned before, the progress made with coruscative inserts suggests that through the use of sophisticatedly shaped charges, or similar launching devices, it will become possible to accelerate colloidal particles to velocities of up to 1,000 kilometers per second. On impact of such ultrafast particles on solid bodies, temperatures of hundreds of millions of degrees will be generated and nuclear fusion reactions ignited in any solid target that contains a sufficient concentration of the light elements mentioned above.

Second Application of the Method of Negation and Construction: The Systematic Discovery of New Phenomena and New Laws of Nature

According to the principles explained in the introduction to this chapter, the following plan often produces remarkable results. To start with, one chooses any dogmatically stated fact or law within the realm of the exact sciences, or from biology, and one investigates where it might lead if he tentatively contests the absolute truth value of such a fact or the universal validity of the law chosen. Proceeding in this bold manner one must nevertheless not overlook the important fact that many of the laws, as they were formulated by our predecessors, often with remarkable and undeniable precision, describe many vast sets of circumtances and events, as they have been investigated by present-day means of observation and experimentation. For this reason the morphologist always concerns himself first with the consideration of extreme conditions, a procedure that assures him of the greatest probability of success in finding positive confirmations for his suspicions. The determined observation of, and the experimentation with, sets of bodies and phenomena under physico-chemical conditions, far different from the ones ordinarily encountered, often yields results that point the way towards discoveries indicating how the old laws must be altered, generalized or even entirely abandoned and replaced by radically new ones. A few examples may serve as illustrations for this type of morphological research.

NEWTON'S LAW OF GRAVITATION

According to Newton two electrically neutral and nonmagnetized solid bodies attract each other with a force that is inversely proportional to the square of their mutual distance. Therefore, if this force is equal to F when the distance between the two centers of mass is equal to D, the same bodies will attract each other with a force $F/4$ if the mutual distance is $2D$, with a force $F/9$ if the distance is $3D$ and so on. This allows us to predict the positions and the movements of the planets with an accuracy so great that during hundreds of years no deviations can be observed, even if we avail ourselves of the most accurate telescopic equipment. Only for Venus and Mercury, the two planets closest to the Sun, the general theory of relativity predicts orbits slightly different from those derived from Newton's theory. Until about 1930, however, the range of validity of Newton's law of gravitation had been tested only for interacting bodies separated by distances smaller than a few light days, that is distances that can be traversed by light in a few days or less.

Since scientists always talk about the "universal" law of gravitation, I asked myself if deviations from this law could not be found if one investigated the interaction of bodies separated by distances very much greater than a few light days. I first found that galaxies separated by millions of light years still attract each other with a force inversely proportional to the square of the distance between them. (It should be remembered that one light year is the distance traversed by light in the course of a year, traveling at a speed of 300,000 km/sec in vacuum.) Going even further I devised tests to find out if the interactions between clusters of galaxies separated by hundreds of millions of light years still can be adequately described by Newton's law. These tests indeed revealed the existence of deviations from the classical theory. It seems that at mutual distances greater than about one-hundred-million light years the attraction between material bodies is much smaller than that predicted by the classical inverse square law. This result suggests forcefully that the general theory of relativity does not represent the last word about gravitation, and that it is in need of being modified in order to come into accord with new observations. At the same time all of the cosmological theories developed during the past several decades on the basis of this theory will have to be abandoned. We therefore have found that, starting from the tentative negation of the absolute validity of Newton's law of gravitation and from the subsequent investigation of the distribution in space and in the velocity field of clusters of galaxies, we have opened up the way towards a considerable widening of our knowledge on the large-scale distribution of matter in the universe and its evolution.

THE NONREVERSIBILITY OF TIME

Both scientists and laymen probably consider it an absolute law of nature that time cannot be reversed in the sense that we shall grow younger all of a sudden. I shall not attempt to show here in which sense an uncompromising morphologist would dare to doubt the absolute truth value of this statement, which to most people appears to be so certain. Indeed, we shall limit ourselves to the discussion of a more modest dogma concerning the supposed irreversibility of time. One of the simplest aspects of this dogma is the belief that we cannot at the present time see ourselves directly as we were and acted many years ago. In his endeavour to deny the absolute truth of this conclusion the morphologist will call upon his knowledge of all available physical and chemical phenomena, and the following thought will suggest itself to him almost automatically. We should indeed be able to literally observe ourselves as we lived and acted in the past, say forty years ago, if an enormous mirror were located at a distance of twenty light years in such a fashion that light, traveling from the earth to this mirror would be reflected back to us. As a matter of fact, I and many of my colleagues think cosmic objects that act like such mirrors actually exist. The morphological visualization of all possible cosmic material aggregates has led us to the recognition of a most interesting large class of ultimately compact bodies. Among these there are, in particular, objects that during their formation liberate such huge amounts of gravitational energy E that the equivalent loss of mass E/c^2 becomes equal to the mass u_0 of our body in its initially completely dispersed state.* The ultimately remaining effective mass in this case will be $\mu = \mu_0 - E/c^2$, a value that, under the limiting circumstances described, is tending towards zero. Such an ultracompact material body of zero effective mass could be accelerated to very high velocities through the action of even very small forces or mechanical impulses. Among these ultimate cosmic bodies the properties of neutron stars and very compact galaxies composed of stars, gases, and light have so far been analyzed theoretically most thoroughly. A typical neutron star, for instance, contains within a sphere of 10 kilometers radius the matter corresponding to thirty suns, so that its mean density is of the order of ten million tons per cubic centimeter. Such massive and dense bodies can deflect beams of light around them through great angles.

As is shown in Figure 27, a signal of light which at the time

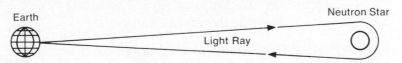

Fig. 27. *Light ray issuing from the Earth and returning to the Earth after being bent around neutron star.*

---

* $c = 300,000$ km/sec is the velocity of light in vacuum.

t_0 starts from the Earth to a neutron star twenty light years away will return to the Earth at the time $t_0 + 40$ years, after having been reversed in direction through the intense gravitational field of the star. In principle, therefore, it is possible to see oneself, literally, as one lived forty years ago by watching the image of the earth as it is being re-enacted for us by that particular neutron star.

The attention of professional physicists may here be called to analogous considerations that can be given to the problem of the universal validity of Coulomb's law and to the conservation of the total electric charge in any closed physical system. Likewise, a morphologist will never be satisfied with the belief that the so-called *uncertainty relations* of quantum mechanics represent an absolute truth. Paradoxically, these relations are, in some sense, of an even more dogmatic character than the principles of classical mechanics inasmuch as they state that the products of certain pairs of physical parameters—such as a coordinate and its corresponding mechanical momentum, or the energy of a given configuration of matter, an atomic or molecular state for instance, and its lifetime—can never be smaller than a certain definite constant, namely Planck's constant. How we must proceed in this case with the application of the method of negation and construction, in order to arrive at a more profound and more generally valid formulation of the laws of atomic physics, cannot be elaborated further in this book, which is primarily intended to be readable for a large circle of readers.

Third Application of the Method of Negation and Construction: The Morphological Evaluation of Individuals and Institutions

In 1952 about fifty directors of research of various large American concerns were invited to a meeting by the University of California at Los Angeles for the purpose of exchanging ideas on the systematic planning of large-scale technical projects. For the successful study of any problem it is obviously necessary to have competent experts available and charge properly qualified organizations with the practical realization of the desired solutions. To choose the right professionals and construction agencies, reliable methods of evaluating men and machines must be developed. Discussions of how that can be done therefore constituted the essential agenda of our meeting. Right at the start one of the participants related how a committee of parliamentarians had visited and inspected the United States Bureau of Standards in Washington, D.C., for about two hours, for the purpose of submitting a report to the United States Congress concerning the value and over-all management of this well-known institution devoted in particular to fundamental research on all standards of measurements being used in the exact sciences, biology, medicine, engineering, food processing, and so on. The gentleman in question added somewhat sneeringly that it was absurd to expect the worthy members of parliament to arrive at any reasonable judgment in such a short time. As the representative of the morphological approach I had to contest this apodeictic opinion categorically. And indeed, any thinker, who as a mental exercise follows up on this negation, will automatically arrive at the following constructive considerations.

As we all well know there often arise situations in life in which, within a fraction of a second, a decision must be reached as to what to do, for instance, in order to avoid an accident or prevent the explosion of a violent conflict among men, say through the insertion of the right word at the right time. In less critical cases there is perhaps a minute, or a day or even a year, at our disposal within which we must reach our decision and act. Morphological research, therefore, has initiated a comprehensive study of the characteristic and most important problem of readying schemata and tests that are concentrates of all available human knowledge and experiences and can or must be applied in many circumstances, both foreseen and unforeseen, if one wishes to achieve optimal results or avoid disasters. This basic problem has not as yet been solved satisfactorily, but the members of the Society for Morphological Research as well as experts of other organizations are working on it.

Choosing the inquiry about the Bureau of Standards as an example, a few possible characteristic tests may be mentioned which illustrate that even a layman might quickly arrive at a partial but significant evaluation. For instance, if one has only a few minutes to investigate the over-all efficiency and reliability of said technical institution for basic research and precision measurements, one might first quickly visit the washroom. There one would casually observe the physicists, chemists, engineers, and their assistants washing their hands. If all of them, before leaving use their paper towels for wiping their respective wash basins clean of any grime, you can be sure you have found a first-class team. No doubt men of this character will work with meticulous care in their laboratories, and we can also expect them to treat their fellow workers and their fellow men anywhere with the proper consideration. Under such circumstances one can further be confident that the physical and chemical constants, as well as other data being determined by the Bureau of Standards, are reliable and all of the work involved is being done speedily and economically. As a matter of fact important additional observations can readily be made in the washroom. For instance, one may notice how many chain smokers there are among the employees and watch their methods of disposing of ashes and cigarette stubs.

If there is more time one might try to meet the director of the institution and observe whether he is a chain smoker and thus a slave of his instincts or not, whether his desk is empty and therefore his brain likewise, whether he speaks several languages or only one and how he expresses himself. Furthermore one might inquire politely what he thinks about his colleagues and employees and which among them he values most, both technically and humanly. One might also spend a few minutes soliciting his opinion about physicists, chemists, and individuals in general, past and present, and whom he thinks to be the greatest. Finally, it is important to test him with the proposal of some project for his institution. Much can be learned from his ensuing reaction: Is his response positive, decisive, and constructive? Or does he immediately decline, using some trite excuse or pretense? Or does he hide himself behind his so-called experts and postpone his decision, pretending that these experts must be consulted first, before he can form an opinion? And if there is still time after one has seen the director, one might want to have a chat with one of the janitors. In many ways such caretakers are the kings in all sorts of matters going on in an institution. It is instructive to find out what authority has been delegated to the janitors, what social standing they have, whether they are liked, and how they are being treated. Still more important may be visits to the safety engineer, the physician and the first aid facilities, as well as a quick survey of all safety installations.

Admittedly this looks like a mixed salad of suggestions. And indeed, this salad is offered here as an appetizer, which will whet the desire for further elaboration by illustrating how morphological research intends to proceed in order to rationally explore all the possibilities for effectively evaluating individuals, technical enterprises and corporations in a more universal and comprehensive manner than hitherto has been used.

6

Special Applications
of the Morphological Methods I:
Propellants

In order to illustrate the method of the morphological box, we have previously discussed the totality of all possible energy transformations in Chapter 4. From the large field of applications of the various energy conversions we select for the present chapter one more restricted area, in order to clearly demonstrate the power of the morphological approach and show that, at the start of almost any large-scale project, specialists are of little use. For this purpose we shall discuss some of the recent developments in the field of propellants, and in particular chemical propellants.

The Morphological Analysis

Whenever possible the morphologist starts with an exact definition of his problem, thus: A propellant on reaction will release energy, which can be used to accelerate a material body with respect to a system of reference relative to which both the body and the propellant were initially at rest; or the energy can be used to propel a vehicle at constant speed through a resisting medium such as air or water. In order to avoid any limitations we shall also consider radiation within an enclosed space as a propellant,

191

which it actually is according to our definition. Indeed, the pressure of the radiation generated within the interior of a supernova, for instance, is capable of ejecting its outer gaseous envelopes with velocities of thousands of kilometers per second into interstellar space, whereby the masses of the gas clouds may be as great as that of the Sun or in some cases even much greater. Man-made phenomena have not as yet reached such cosmic proportions. Nevertheless the radiative energies released from nuclear bombs are great enough to set material bodies in motion, which according to terrestrial standards are considerable. The energy actually stored in a propellant may belong to any one of the ten types discussed in Chapter 4, that is it can be kinetic, elastic, or gravitational energy, heat, electrical and magnetic energy, radiation, chemical potential energy, nuclear energy, or the rest energy of the elementary particles.

Liberation of any one of these types of energy stored in a propellant can be used to accelerate a material body that is in contact with it. In classical technology the designation *propellant* was usually applied to two types of substances only, namely those that store either heat or chemical energy. In the future, however, we shall also deal with nuclear propellants storing nuclear energy that can be liberated and applied for propulsion.

In the present book, however, we restrict ourselves to a survey of chemical propellants only, the discovery, analysis, and industrial production of which, during the past three decades, has been marked by a precipitous and ever-accelerated development because of the contingencies of World War II and the subsequent start of the Space Age. It is a most remarkable fact that the professional chemists, during this frantic race, have contributed very little towards the invention of new propellants. On the other hand many of the decisive advances were achieved with the aid of the morphological approach as it first was applied more than forty years ago. This is due to the fact that the initial and all comprehensive occupation with the general problems of propellants, if it is to be successful, must be *integral research*, which requires a far more universal outlook than that which is being taught students of chemistry at the various universities at the present time and as it will be illustrated by a few examples here.

First of all we note that there is really no ideal all-around propellant optimally suited to the activation of all types of propulsive power plants. It depends on the particular circumstances and boundary conditions which propellant will satisfy certain minimum or maximum requirements. Examples of desired specifications for instance are those that respectively refer to the available energy per gram or to the energy per cubic centimeter of the propellant. Of interest for today's high priority applications are only those combinations of chemical reagents that, either per gram or per cubic centimeter, can liberate more than one kilocalorie, that is enough heat to evaporate two grams of water or raise the temperature of one liter of water by one degree Celsius. Further requirements apply to the reaction speed, the safety of handling, the durability and availability, the behaviour during transport when exposed to heat, cold, shocks, and so on. For all of these reasons a morphological analysis is most desirable, and in our opinion indispensable, if one wishes to find the best propellant for any specific application. How numerous and complex the various requirements are that chemical propellants must satisfy in order to be useful for all of the various applications can be gathered from the following brief reviews.

TRANSFORMATION OF CHEMICAL ENERGY INTO KINETIC ENERGY

Chemical Energy → Heat → Kinetic Energy

When chemical propellants react, heat is being liberated. This heat can be transformed into kinetic energy by means of expanding gases, which cool in the process. The adiabatic expansion of hot steam or of hot gases, for instance, is being used in steam and gas turbines or in reciprocating engines and in rockets to put the turbine wheels, the pistons or the rockets themselves into motion.

Man and beast manage to oxydize food within their bodies at

essentially constant temperatures, that is they convert chemical energy *isothermally* into mechanical, elastic or kinetic energy, Remarkably enough this type of energy transformation, which nature accomplishes with the greatest of ease, has not yet been possible with the aid of any large-scale device constructed by man.

Chemical Energy → Electrical Energy → Kinetic Energy

In principle it is possible to convert the chemical energy of propellants directly into electrical energy, which then can readily be used to set material bodies in motion. This happens, for instance, when we crank the engines of our automobiles with the aid of the electro-chemical batteries installed for the purpose. As in the case of the thermomechanical conversion discussed above, the electro-mechanical process may be conducted either isothermally, or adiabatically with an initial sharp rise in temperature and subsequent cooling. We shall later on return to this problem when we discuss the possibilities of the so-called *propellant-flow-batteries* or *powercells*.

THE ROLE OF THE MEDIUM THROUGH WHICH THE PROPULSIVE POWER PLANT MOVES

As long as we live and operate on the Earth, there are four essential media which we must consider. These are the *atmosphere* and beyond it, for practical purposes, a *vacuum*. Furthermore we are interested in vehicles that move submerged in the ocean or other bodies of *water*, and finally we want to construct vehicles that are self-propelled and capable of forcing their way through the *solid earth*. Propellants that can propel vehicles through the four media mentioned without involving the latter in the power-producing chemical reactions are called *self-contained propellants*. Since only these can accelerate rockets in a vacuum, they are usually designated as rocket propellants.

Propellants that are specifically suited for the activation of air-, water-, or earth-"breathing" engines we propose to call aeropropellants (or, more prosaically and simply, fuels), hydropropellants or hydrofuels, and terrapropellants or terrafuels.

Whereas rocket propellants contain all the chemical compounds needed for the generation of the necessary propulsive energy, the aero, hydro, and terrapropellants can furnish this energy only when reacted in combination with either air, water, or with the various components which make up the crust or the interior strata of the Earth.

TYPES OF POWER PLANTS TO BE ACTIVATED BY THE VARIOUS PROPELLANTS

A device that carries with it the chemical reagents necessary and sufficient for its propulsion we propose here to designate for short as a *vehicle*. It may be a manned or an unmanned device. A body being launched without carrying its own propellant we shall call a *missile* or a *projectile*.

Generally speaking, vehicles are being set in motion by propellants that react relatively slowly, while bullets, shells, and projectiles in general are shot from rifles, cannons and shaped charges by means of fast-reacting and even detonating explosives.

In order to differentiate further among various propellants we speak respectively of those used for the activation of *stationary* power plants on the one hand and *propulsive* power plants on the other. In stationary power engines chemical energy is released and reacted into rotational or oscillational kinetic energy. These engines, of course, may also be used to move various types of vehicles such as locomotives, automobiles, ships, and airplanes. This can be accomplished by connecting them with wheels, water wheels, or propellers, whose reactions with the surrounding medium, air, or water generate the desired forward thrust. The true propulsive power plants, however, such as the rockets in vacuum, the *aeroturbojets* in the air, the *hydroturbojets* under water, and the *terrapulses* which are designed to bore through the solid earth, generally convert chemical energy into kinetic energy of fast gaseous, liquid, or solid exhaust jets, whose reactions on the walls of the respective reaction chambers generate the necessary propulsive thrusts.

PHYSICAL CHARACTERISTICS OF PROPELLANTS

Without going into too many details we may first differentiate between gaseous, liquid, and solid propellants. In the case of air-breathing engines, which are in the great majority, it would be most desirable if one could use solid coal as the fuel in order to achieve maximum economy. This, however, has not so far been feasible since coal cannot as yet be used for the activation of high grade propulsive powerplants. Its use even in the case of many stationary power plants, such as the gasturbines, is compounded with great difficulties. The prospects of using coal as a fuel for aeroturbojets of aeroplanes are therefore very poor indeed. Gaseous propellants on the other hand are easy to handle, but uneconomical for purposes of propulsion because of the necessity of heavy containers. They are therefore useful, so far, only for certain types of stationary installations, which are located near supplies of the gaseous fuels.

Solved and Unsolved Problems of Chemical Propellants

In order to briefly survey the many problems about propellants that have been solved, as well as some of those remaining to be investigated, we proceed here to discuss separately some of the characteristics of the four fundamental classes of propellants mentioned before.

AEROPROPELLANTS

It is well known that enormous efforts have been made in the past to discover coal and oil deposits, since except for wood, both coal and oil represent the major fuels of the pre-atomic age. The methods of exploration and exploitation of oil fields sum up to a first-class technological detective story. We cannot here, however, go into any details about these fascinating activities, and we only touch briefly on some of the interesting problems currently being investigated. Among these the numerous efforts at refining the naturally occurring fuel supplies like wood, coal, and oil are obviously of prime importance, not only for the generation of mechanical and electrical power, but also for the production of innumerable artificial products, such as plastics, solvents, soaps, perfumes, and so on.

The refining of crude oils on the one hand aims at the production of high-grade fuels, such as octane (C_8H_{18}) for use in combustion engines; as important side-products sulphur, asphalt, and many other materials may also be obtained. Parenthetically it should perhaps be mentioned that throughout World War II we produced, at the Aerojet Engineering Corporation in Azusa, hundreds of thousands of rocket engines (Jatos) for jet-assisted take-off of fighter planes and bombers, using mixtures of asphalt and potassium perchlorate as the main solid propellant.

A further important goal to be achieved is completeness of all combustion processes, that is highest thermodynamic efficiency, as well as elimination of exhausts containing partially reacted and dangerous reaction products. These requirements often confront the physicist, the chemist, and the engineer with rather serious problems. For those of us who live in southern California, and particuarly in the Los Angeles area, these issues are of vital importance, since no relief seems to be in sight for our suffering from the effects of deadly formations of smog, which frequently hover over the whole territory as a consequence of the unchecked ejection of noxious fumes from millions of automobiles. (We have already touched on these unfortunate circumstances.)

One of the most important problems of fuel chemistry for the future concerns the realization of propellant-flow-batteries or power cells. These are devices designed to convert chemical energy directly and continuously into electrical energy. The ordinary closed and self-contained electrical batteries, of course, actually achieve this conversion, but they produce only small amounts of energy: They do not work continuously for long periods of time, and they must often be recharged and regenerated. Also they are not very durable. A propellant-flow-battery, on the other hand, generates electric current as long as the proper components of a chemical propellant are pumped into it. One of the really urgent problems in this field calls for the development and production of power cells that "consume" inflowing coal, gasoline, kerosene, or oil at one electrode, while the other electrode is being fed with atmospheric oxygen. The fuel is oxydized by the available oxygen in a proper electrolyte that carries the electric current, such that the available heat (or rather the free enthalpy) is directly converted into electrical energy. In spite of the herculean efforts made by leading men of research for almost a century, it has not yet been possible to solve the problem of the direct large-scale production of electrical energy from chemical reactions under avoidance of any intervening process of generation of heat. Inasmuch as no fundamental physical laws are known that stand in the way of such a direct conversion, and since devices of small capacity can actually be operated with an almost ideal efficiency, we may expect that power cells that generate large currents through the reaction of carbon or of hydrocarbons with the oxygen of the air will eventually become possible. The solution of this old problem will be of the greatest importance for industry, since it will then become possible to produce electrical current exceedingly cheaply and conduct electrical power over great distances with very small losses. Today the overland transmissions still operate very inefficiently with a most cumbersome and expensive chain of processes, that is the transformation of chemical energy into heat, followed by the conversion of this heat into mechanical energy (for instance in a gas or steam turbine), and finally the generation of electrical energy from the mechanical energy driving an electrical generator. One of the most desirable by-products of the power cells for use in automobiles would of course lie in the automatic elimination of the presently highly objectionable noxious exhaust products.

ROCKET PROPELLANTS

Rocket propellants, just as explosives, are self-contained combinations. In other words they contain all the chemical reagents that on reaction will produce the final reaction products at pressures and temperatures capable of exerting the necessary thrust for the propulsion of rockets. A rocket propellant can therefore be made of a fuel and an oxydizer in the right proportion, which does not need to be stoichiometric and actually seldom is. The reaction takes place in a thrust chamber and the reaction products, a part of which must be gaseous, are expanded on exit through a properly shaped nozzle, as a result of which they cool while heat is being transformed into kinetic energy of the exhaust jets. Interest in the synthesis of ever more energetic rocket propellants has been growing by leaps and bounds during the past two decades because of the military requirements and because of extended plans for the march into space. The efforts made have already resulted in outlays of funds of tens of billion of dollars. From a universal vantage point the following developments stand out in marked relief:

For different types of applications either gaseous, liquid, or solid propellants may be most desirable. *Solid propellants* are particularly suitable for the production of short duration thrusts, such as they are needed for artillery rockets, for assisted takeoff rockets (Jatos), or for launchers and booster rockets which may be used as "first stages" for the initial acceleration of large space rockets. Jatos and booster rockets are usually jetisoned after burnout. Of the latter, some are now being built that, for a period of a few seconds, can exert a thrust of thousands of tons. *Liquid propellants* on the other hand are most suitable for the generation of thrusts of long duration. Their great advantage resides in the fact that only relatively small thrust chambers are needed, and the propellant tanks can be light weight. And finally, *gaseous propellants* are used for the activation of auxiliary devices that will achieve all sorts of small-scale operations. *Hybrid* motors, using aluminum and water as their main propellant combination, for instance, promise to become of major importance for operations on the Moon and actually may facilitate the return flights to the Earth, since the materials necessary can all be produced from the rocks available on the lunar surface.

As to the problem of producing propellants that per unit weight can release a maximum amount of energy, or propellants that achieve the same in the smallest volume, the following developments have taken place.

USE OF CONVENTIONAL CHEMICAL REAGENTS

Among these, alcohol and liquid oxygen were perhaps the first ones used on a large scale, for instance for the activation of the German V-2 rocket, which achieved exhaust velocities of about 2,300 meters per second. The greater the velocity of the exhaust gases, which in the case of the V-2 were CO_2, CO, H_2O, and H_2, the greater is the specific thrust obtained and the greater is the forward acceleration of the rocket.

As a solid propellant, combination mixture of asphalt and potassium perchlorate has been extensively used in the United States of America. More recently polystyrenes and polyurethane with ammoniumperchlorate have come into use, because the latter oxydizer does not produce any opaque exhaust clouds, at least not in dry weather.

In order to save space and eliminate duplication of many of the auxiliary devices of jet engines, such as pumps, feed lines, and injectors, monopropellants were invented and introduced. Among these, nitromethane was first promoted by the author in 1943 and probably was the first one ever used in rocket technology.

THE SYNTHESIS AND PRODUCTION OF HIGH ENERGY PROPELLANTS

In order to travel into interplanetary space, that is, to achieve an escape velocity from the Earth of about 11.2 km/sec one has so far been forced to use a cluster of several stage rockets. It is therefore of the greatest importance that one find and produce rocket propellants that will achieve a far greater exhaust velocity than the currently available ones of about 2.5 km/sec.

Propellants whose fuel components are made of various compounds of carbon, however, have been shown to be incapable of generating exhaust velocities greater than about 3 km/sec. Therefore, if one wishes to obtain higher specific impulses, one must replace the carbon by some other light element. Among these, boron is one of the most promising. In fact, aluminiumborohydride, $Al(BH_4)_3$, for instance, can be reacted with liquid fluorine to produce an exhaust velocity and a specific impulse about 50 per cent greater than any of the conventional propellant combinations using carbon fuels.

FRAGMENT CHEMISTRY

In the course of a systematic search for ever more powerful propellants it occurred to me that much could be gained if one succeeded in stabilizing monoatomic hydrogen H, the imine group NH, the amino group NH_2, or radicals and fragments such as CH, CH_2, CH_3 and others in macroscopic bulk density.

Today the prospects are excellent that we shall eventually succeed in stabilizing the mentioned fragments at macroscopic densities either at low temperatures, in magnetic fields, or trapped within certain solid crystal lattices. Success along any of these lines would enable us to produce combinations that, per gram or per cubic centimeter, would release from five to ten times the energy that can be generated by any of the now commonly used propellants and that would allow us to launch single-stage rockets free from the gravitational pull of the Earth.

The development of fragment chemistry is also of the greatest importance for the field of energy storage and would in addition make it possible to transport energy in concentrated form, avoiding the presently sustained heavy losses in the transmission of electrical energy. Progress in the field of fragment chemistry is therefore of great importance, with a view to many different terrestrial applications as well as for extraterrestrial operations.

METACHEMISTRY

There are molecules that appear to be stable but can disintegrate under certain conditions. The molecules of acetylene C_2H_2 are of this kind, which on decomposition into $2C + H_2$ will release about two kilocalories per gram of initial substance. Since the carbon, however, appears in its solid phase among the reaction products, as well as for some additional reasons, pure acetylene is quite unusable as a propellant, and it must be mixed with ammonia, for instance, for the purpose. The search for similar *metastable molecules* has in the meantime led to the discovery of some most interesting chemical compounds.

Among the metastable molecules, helium hydride HeH is particularly promising as a potential high energy monopropellant. Of course HeH does not exist as a normal and stable isolated molecule, but it is dynamically stable in some of its "excited" states. Upon disintegration into helium and hydrogen it will release a very much greater heat of reaction (or more properly free enthalpy) than any of the currently used propellants. In addition, the gaseous reaction products obtained have some most desirable characteristics, which make it possible to transform the heat released with maximum efficiency into kinetic energy.

Attention should also be called to the fact that the study of fragment chemistry and metachemistry leads to insights of importance for our understanding of the detailed kinetic processes taking place in all chemical reactions and sorely in need of elucidation. Radicals and various other fragments of molecules and their ions, as well as various metastable molecules play a great role in many cosmic processes and particularly in those which take place in the atmospheres of the stars and planets, as well as in interstellar gas and dust clouds.

The occupation with the chemistry of propellants thus leads us to an understanding of the constitution and the transformations of matter in the microscopic, macroscopic, and cosmic world, which is obviously of importance in a vast number of fields including organic chemistry, biology, medicine, and astrophysics.

TERRAPROPELLANTS

We here deal with chemicals capable of reacting with various minerals, and which in these reactions, liberate both enough energy and gaseous reaction products that can be harnessed in properly designed terrajet engines, such as the terrapulse, to move them through the solid earth, whereby jets of hot liquid and gaseous "slags" are being ejected towards the rear.

In contradistinction to aero- and hydrofuels, the terrapropellants need not be, chemically speaking, only reducing agents. They can also "overoxydize" the solid medium (earth) through which they travel and thus liberate gaseous oxygen and heat in their reaction with the components of this medium. Liquid fluorine is therefore a terrafuel, while it can not readily be used as either an aerofuel or a hydrofuel.

As we already indicated on page 152 it may be confidently predicted that terrajet engines will be built in the near future and used in the search for and exploitation of new oil, coal, metal, and mineral deposits. Their most important role, however, may well be the exploration of the interiors of the Earth and the Moon, especially since on the latter we shall be forced to live underground for most of the time.

THE OUTLOOK FOR SMALL COUNTRIES

The citizens of small nations often complain that their countries are not large enough and their resources not sufficient to allow them to participate effectively in the work on atomic energy and the preparations for the march into outer space. Since I never felt that such a negative attitude is justified, I advise the small countries to start with modest but significant research on the chemistry of propellants, methods of igniting nuclear fusion, instrumentation of all sorts, and theoretical planning. Without basic knowledge large countries and their giant projects cannot make any decisive progress either. Through the mastery of propellant chemistry, for instance, a small country can very well make a major contribution to the technological progress in the world. I hope in particular that my own native Switzerland will multiply its efforts in the field of inorganic and physical chemistry, which today are poor but might very well eventually reach the same high level as Switzerland's organic chemistry and in particular its astounding achievements in the invention, synthesis, and production of pharmaceuticals.

7

Special Applications
of the Morphological Methods II:
Astronomy

Hoping that the reader who has patiently read through this book up to this point will have found some useful suggestions, the author, both as an enthusiastic astronomer and a morphologist now proposes to discuss, in this chapter exclusively, some special topics concerning the history of astronomy, that is, our present knowledge of the universe, the astronomical instruments, the problems confronting us and the practical importance of this science. Although special technical problems are being discussed we shall try to show that the morphological approach is still clearly in evidence. In addition, some understanding of the subjects discussed here is necessary for a true appreciation of the plans proposed in this chapter, which concern one of the greatest adventures of our time, man's March into the Universe, some of whose morphological aspects will be presented.

Although astronomy is the oldest of the natural sciences it has actually never been quite realistically appraised by a larger public. Concerning the scientific and the human value of astronomical research, the layman, the professionals in all fields, who are not astronomers, and occasionally even the astronomers themselves have become the victims of harebrained notions and conclusions. One might even go so far as to claim that the true progress of mankind runs parallel with the overcoming of false and superstitious beliefs about the nature of cosmic objects and phenomena, a view which should inspire and encourage astronomers to ever greater efforts in behalf of man.

Unfortunately the professional astronomers are themselves subject to various aberrations of the mind, which are just as dangerous as those responsible for the irrational behaviour of so many of the uneducated and unbalanced men. In the first place, many astronomers often act haughtily and refuse to enlighten the public about astronomy's real worth. In fact, judging from my own long experience, many among them do not really know it themselves. Also, time and again the progress of astronomy has been retarded for decades and even for centuries because this or that bigwig had developed theories or produced results that later on proved to be completely false, but which, because of his power and influence as well as other all-too human circumstances, enslaved or stifled independent research or drove it into sterile channels. These conclusions are well illustrated by the fact that astronomy in one country after another flourished and then degenerated, as it happened with the Poland of Copernicus, Tycho Brahe's Denmark, Kepler's Germany, Galileo's Italy, the England of Newton, Halley and the Herschels, the Russia of the Struves, the France of Cassini and Leverrier, and most recently the America of George Ellery Hale. In this connection it is rather remarkable that Switzerland, in spite of having produced some of the greatest theoreticians—I think of Leonhard Euler, Johann Jakob Balmer, Walter Ritz, R. Emden and Albert Einstein—never, had any practical astronomy to speak of. A Swiss himself, the author may be permitted to hazard a guess that, because of a change of outlook by many of his young countrymen, Switzerland may finally hope to put an end to this unsatisfactory state of affairs and enjoy (and bemoan) a development marked by the usual rise to great heights followed by the apparently inevitable degeneration. I should be most pleased, however, if my co-citizens were to catch up with some of the other nations in their march into outer space, and if in particular they were to occupy themselves with the human implications, not only of astronomical, but of all scientific and technological progress.

We now proceed to discuss, first, some of the most important achievements of scientific astronomy, and second, a few of the practical and sociological aspects. Finally, in this chapter a few thoughts will be devoted to the problems of the space age.

Classical Astronomy

THE EARTHBOUND OBSERVER

We first call attention to the important limitation that until a few years ago neither the astronomers themselves nor their instruments could be transported high enough above the surface of the Earth to succeed in eliminating the disturbing effects of the atmosphere. These effects are essentially fourfold in character. In the first place, the atmosphere is transparent only for visual light and for radio waves in the approximate wavelength range of from one centimeter to about thirty meters. Second, bad "seeing," that is turbulence, shock waves, and other disturbances, even in very clear weather, cause serious distortions and fluctuations in brightness of the images of stars and other cosmic objects when observed with the large and most powerful telescopes. Third, astronomical observations are completely stopped by bad weather. Fourth, the night sky is never really dark because of the permanent "sky glow" emanating from the ionosphere, and finally, it is not possible to work in daytime because the sunlight, scattered in all directions by the elements of the atmosphere, renders the sky so luminous that, except for the Sun and the brightest stars, no celestial objects can be seen. The radioastronomers, on the other hand, can work around the clock through the whole day.

The earthbound astronomers have lived through the following periods of development.

FROM ANTIQUITY TO GALILEO

Before Galileo, astronomers had to do without optical instruments. All observations had to be made with the unaided eye. Today we can only marvel at the achievements of the ancient astronomers: Among these are the compilations of exact catalogues of stars, including valuable estimates of their relative apparent brightness, the determination of the circumference of the Earth, methods for measuring the distances to the Moon and the Sun, the visualization of the "geographically" correct picture of the successive relative configurations of the Sun, the Moon, and the planets, and finally the extraordinary penetrating analysis of the motion of the axis of the Earth, which causes the precession of the equinoxes and the motion of the celestial pole. The end of this period is marked by the epoch-making achievement of Copernicus (1473–1543), who clearly recognized that the Earth is not the center of the universe but just one among the planets circling around the Sun.

FROM GALILEO TO ABOUT 1910

As a consequence of the invention of the first refractor, by Galileo (1564–1642), and later of the first reflecting telescope, by Newton (1642–1727), astronomy made tremendous progress. Many new celestial objects were discovered in rapid succession. Furthermore it later became possible to investigate the physical and chemical properties of the Sun, the stars, and other cosmic objects through the use of many newly invented instruments. The most important one among these is the spectroscope, introduced by Bunsen (1811–99) and Kirchhoff (1824–87), with which the spectrum of the Sun was first analyzed, and which enables us today to investigate the chemical composition of both luminous and dark matter, even in some of the most distant galaxies.

In the "geographical" exploration of the universe the second decisive breakthrough was made by Giordano Bruno (1548?–1600), who was the first to recognize clearly that the universe is not limited to the solar system and the stars themselves are self-luminous bodies populating an enormously extended cosmic space, the Milky Way or our galaxy. In recognition of his great revelations Giordano Bruno was burned at the stake by the Church. The diameter of the Milky Way system, the existence of which Bruno first visualized, is now being estimated at about 100,000 light years.

During the period under discussion, Galileo, the Herschels and Leverrier discovered the first moons of Jupiter and the planets Uranus and Neptune. The Herschels, father and son, surveyed the Milky Way in depth for stars and nebulae, some of which are interstellar gas clouds excited to fluorescence by radiation from neighboring stars, while others were shown later to be extra-galactic stellar systems. Developing the theory, Galileo and Newton formulated the basic laws of mechanics and gravitation, which during the following two centuries were refined and applied by the great mathematicians Lagrange, Euler, and Laplace, who were successful in predicting the motions of the planets with great accuracy for centuries to come. At the same time Halley made the most important discovery that the stars move relative to one another, and Bessel, by means of direct triangulation, determined the first absolute distance of any star (61 Cygni).

Modern Astronomy

THE PERIOD FROM 1910 TO THE PRESENT

The past sixty years brought, on the one hand, the invention and construction of many novel and most useful instruments including the giant optical telescopes, the radio telescopes and the photoelectronic and photoelectric devices. On the other hand rapid progress was made in theoretical and experimental physics, which enabled us to gain deeper insights into the nature of the various celestial bodies and phenomena. Particularly important is recognition that the enormous energies liberated in the stars are in great part produced by processes of nuclear fusion, which transforms protons and electrons into helium and many other nuclei of the heavier elements.

A few years after this period of the astronomical exploration of space the third important "geographical" breakthrough was made by the great Swedish astronomer Knut Lundmark (1889–1958), who showed in 1918 that the cosmic space beyond the confines of the Milky Way, that is extragalactic space, is populated by innumerable stellar systems, the most giant ones of which, like our own Milky Way galaxy, contain billions of stars. Lundmark was also the first to determine the distance of the great nebula in Andromeda, the only galaxy (except our own) that can readily be seen by the unaided eye. His result was 650,000 light years, a distance which, because of new data now available, had to be tripled in the recent past. The most distant galaxies that can be photographed with the 200-inch Palomar Hale telescope are located at estimated distances of about 5 billion light years.

The question now arises of what the next step will be in our exploration of the "geography" of the universe. The answer to this question will materially depend on the solution of the problem of whether or not the universe is expanding, as most astronomers believe it to be. The idea of the expansion of the universe has its origin on the one hand in certain observational facts and is derived on the other hand from Einstein's general theory of relativity. One observes indeed that, generally speaking, the characteristic spectra of galaxies are shifted towards the red by amounts roughly proportioned to the distances of the galaxies in question. Perhaps the simplest explanation of this fact is to assume a general and continuing expansion of the universe, that is to relate the red shift to the Doppler effect of light emitted from sources moving away from us, in this case the galaxies. There are, nevertheless, certain conclusions that can be derived from this hypothesis, which so far cannot be confirmed, and which seem even to contradict certain well-established facts.

We are therefore still confronted with the unanswered question of whether ten billion years ago the universe was really very much smaller than today, or it is much older than most astronomers are willing to admit. I am inclined to think that this problem will be solved in the near future on the basis of results now rapidly being accumulated, which refer in particular to the character of the material contents of the universe and to its large-scale distribution. A few of the basic facts already known will be briefly sketched in the following section.

PERMANENT AND TEMPORARY COSMIC BODIES

Among the more permanent cosmic bodies, three types, that is, the stars, the galaxies, and the clusters of galaxies, are the most outstanding. Everyone of these material aggregates can only grow to a certain size. Just like the trees they cannot indefinitely "grow into the sky." Stars more massive than about one hundred suns probably cannot exist, since for such bodies the pressures and temperatures in their centers assume values at which the energy generation by nuclear reactions increases at a rate that will cause the surface layers to "evaporate." Galaxies composed of luminous stars may perhaps reach masses equal to ten million million (10^{13}) suns. At this stage the stars in the central cores of such systems are getting packed so closely that their mutual radiation begins to evaporate them, while at the same time they will be disrupted because of the tidal effects during mutual close encounters or collisions. And finally the largest clusters of galaxies may contain up to about 100,000 members, at which limit the individual stellar systems begin to disrupt each other as a result of frequent close encounters, just as in the world of atoms, molecules, crystals, and living organisms, the sizes and masses of the celestial bodies are limited because of the emergence, at certain stages of growth, of characteristic destructive effects.

In addition to the more or less permanent bodies, the universe is populated by a multitude of variable and short-lived objects. Among these there are formations short-lived in character, such as the interstellar and intergalactic gas and dust clouds in the tremendous spaces between the stars and the galaxies. Most interesting are the various supernovae, novae and eruptive stars of all kinds, which are all very specific and mostly short-lived types. The study of supernovae in particular promises to become of great importance for our understanding of cosmic events in general, because of the stupendous processes that take place in them within a few days, that is conversions of matter and energy, which in the case of ordinary permanent stars, require hundreds of millions of years for their completion. The brightest supernovae, during a few days after outburst, have a maximum absolute luminosity equalling billions of times that of the Sun. Because of this fact supernovae can be used as easily recognizable "landmarks" and will eventually allow us to survey the universe to distances of billions of light years. This was one of our reasons for organizing the International Committee for Research on Supernovae at the assembly of the International Astronomical Union in Berkeley, California, in August, 1961.

Supernovae and their remnants also emit cosmic rays and radio waves. The total intensity of the cosmic rays, as compared with that of light in interstellar space, is relatively very great. It may therefore be conjectured that the radiation from supernovae—one of which probably flares up in our galaxy on an average of once every hundred years, and some of which must have been quite near to the solar system—may at least in part be responsible for the mutations of species among the plants and animals, that is those sudden jumps in evolution that are responsible for the emergence of new genetic types, forms, and families among the living formations of matter.

Under certain extraordinary circumstances the gas clouds ejected from some types of supernovae with velocities of more than 10,000 km/sec may induce nuclear fusion reactions in the surrounding interstellar matter or in neighboring stars. The resulting "chains of supernovae" and implosions of compact galaxies into "neutron star-studded compact galaxies" and "neutron star-studded cosmic balls of light" are probably among the most gigantic events taking place in the cosmos. It is estimated that in such eruptions amounts of energy are liberated capable of launching ten thousand stars into cosmic space with velocities of hundreds of kilometers per second. If such ejections occur asymmetrically, they may produce jets and counterjets, all sorts of interstellar and intergalactic cloud formations as well as the remarkable taffylike intergalactic "bridges" between neighboring galaxies.

The frequency of the occurrence of supernovae in an individual large galaxy, on the average, is of the order of one per several hundred years. The last well-observed supernovae in our more immediate "neighborhood" within the Milky Way system are those of 1054 A.D. (observed by the Chinese, the Japanese, and the Persians in the constellation of Taurus), Tycho's star of 1572, Kepler's star of 1604, and perhaps Eta Carinae of 1843, which appears to have been an object of Zwicky's type V. The remnant of the Chinese supernova of 1054 A.D. now forms the famous Crab Nebula (Messier 1), an enormous cloud of rapidly expanding and fluorescing gases. Both this remnant and those of other supernovae have been found to be sources of radio waves and cosmic rays. In spite of the fact that the appearance of comets, meteors, and the appearance and dissolution of sun spots had been observed thousands of years ago, which should have suggested to any discerning investigator that changes are taking place in extraterrestrial space, most of the scholars of antiquity and of the Middle Ages believed that the stars were immutable. We need only refer to Tycho Brahe himself, undoubtedly one of the greatest observers of all time, who wrote of the supernova of 1572, "It was a miracle, and even the greatest of miracles that have occurred in the whole range of nature since the beginning of the world, or one certainly to be classed with those attested by the Holy Oracles, the staying of the Sun in its course in answer to the prayers of Joshua and the darkening of the Sun's face at the time of Crucifixion." Parenthetically, as a possible test for the existence somewhere else in the universe of life as we know it on Earth, I suggest that, as far as I am aware, so far only the study of novalike eruptions indicates any practical procedure. It is indeed exceedingly improbable that a "dead" planet such as the Earth could implosively neutron star although it is both nuclearly and gravitationally at best in a pseudostable configuration. Such spontaneous implosions can probably only be made to occur by intelligent beings, who, after having mastered the problem of nuclear fusion ignition of common materials on a large scale, could in principle and suddenly transform itself, with the liberation of immense amounts of energy, into a ball of iron or an ultradense pygmy or explode the Earth and other similar bodies either by diabolic intention or through some unfortunate mistake in experimentation. Should we searchers for supernovae and other eruptive events in the cosmos discover events that can be explained only by the assumption that they represent the results of implosions and explosions of bodies similar to the Earth, we should be forced to conclude that living beings of highly developed intelligence are the instigators and that they have put a flaming end to their existence either because of some miscalculations or because their pathological aberrations got the better of them and made them intentionally commit genocide. In this connection it should again be emphasized that the observational search for eruptive events in the universe is one of the voluminous tasks for whose solution the cooperation of amateurs with the professional astronomers is urgently needed.

CONDITIONS IN THE UNIVERSE, NEAR AND FAR

The asymmetry of time is one of the most fundamental phenomena governing our lives. Time runs seemingly imperturbably and unalterably in one direction, from birth to death. The same is true for the course of all life, as well as for the evolution of the physico-chemical character of the Earth as a whole during the past five billion years. Extrapolating, we therefore are inclined to conclude that the whole universe also has a history that is irreversible and that it does not represent a statistically stationary state analogous, for instance, to a gas of diatomic molecules in thermodynamic equilibrium in which the number of molecules dissociating per second on the average is the same as the number of molecules being formed per second through the association of the two atoms constituting them. According to practically all the modern cosmological theories the universe is assumed to have such a history, inasmuch as most of them postulate that the so-called universal cosmological red shift in the spectra of the distant galaxies must be interpreted as a Doppler shift due to a general expansion of the universe. As already mentioned, this simple hypothesis is not entirely beyond reproach, since the following important observational facts cannot easily be reconciled with it.

1. The largest and most extended material aggregates in the universe, such as the clusters of galaxies both near and far, that is in regard to distances, as they can be explored with the 200-inch Hale telescope, are, in all observable aspects, of the same morphological characters, both qualitatively and quantitatively.

2. The chemical composition, that is the relative abundances of the various elements, is the same for similar types of celestial objects both near and far.

3. The distribution and the space density of all large-scale objects is the same at all distances that can be explored with the largest telescopes. This is true in particular for the rich compact clusters of galaxies that are the largest characteristic agglomerations of matter known so far.

4. Matter in the universe at all distances seems to be subject to the same physical laws.

5. Extended observations and the statistical analysis of about 8,000 clusters of galaxies distributed over large areas of the sky indicate that there exist no clusters of clusters of galaxies as one should expect to find them if Newton's law of gravitation and the principles of the general theory of relativity were strictly and universally true. The new findings therefore suggest that the theory of gravitation needs to be reformulated and the bases of all cosmological theories must be re-examined.

POSSIBLE MODELS OF THE UNIVERSE

Neither the men of research nor the laymen seem to bring themselves to abstain from speculating in vain about the origin and evolution of the universe instead of occupying themselves constructively with the more pressing immediate problems of life. In order to offer the general public at least some tangible information, therefore, we briefly review here some of the possible cosmological theories professional astronomers are considering, although we do not know if any of them actually correctly represents the real facts.

Hypothesis A

The universe is evolving in a *unidirectional way*. It started expanding about ten billion years ago from an initial state of extreme concentration of all matter and radiation, and it continues to expand today at a rate that will double the average distances between the galaxies in our neighborhood in about ten billion years. The ages of the oldest stars in our Milky Way system are also of the order of ten billion years. New stars, however, are still being formed from the interstellar and perhaps the intergalactic gas clouds.

Hypothesis B

The universe is much older than the ten billion years generally assumed and has now reached a *stationary state*, which by some authors has been called the state of the *thermodynamic heat death*. According to this hypothesis, all changes in this model of the universe are relatively local in character. Even long-time events, such as the evolution of the Earth, and the formation and destruction of stars, galaxies and clusters of galaxies, are to be interpreted as nothing more than normal statistical fluctuations in a system in thermodynamic equilibrium. Although these fluctuations may assume cosmic dimensions, they are nevertheless nothing more than giant analogues of the microscopic fluctuations that occur in the gas in thermodynamic equilibrium discussed above.

Hypothesis C

Although the universe is expanding, all local conditions remain forever the same and are locally stationary, since matter is assumed to be uniformly and continually created throughout space, for example, neutrons, protons and electrons emerging from nothing. This hypothesis of the so-called *steady state universe* and the notion of continuous creation was conceived by the British mathematicians Bondi, Hoyle, Gold and McCrea to avoid some of the difficulties afflicting the hypotheses A and B. In my opinion the steady state theory cannot really account for the major facts known. And, what is more important, it is no theory at all, scientifically speaking, because as Einstein once said "The good Lord may be very sophisticated but he is not malicious." This means that he does not try to fool the poor men of research with any tricks, like suddenly creating something out of nothing. In order to facilitate things for my mentioned British colleagues, I should propose that we go even further and admit from the start that stars, galaxies and clusters of galaxies are being created instantaneously from nothing, all at the proper time and proper rate, since by this bold hypothesis we can easily overcome all the difficult theoretical problems confronting us. And anyway, it would seem that the good Lord can create galaxies from nothing just as easily as He can create neutrons.

OUTLOOK

With many novel instruments at his disposal, and especially with the aid of radio telescopes, photoelectronic telescopes, and rocket-borne instrumentation, as well as from observatories to be built presently on the Moon, astronomers may expect to make faster progress than almost any of the other scientists. A systematic survey of the universe for all the possible microscopic, macroscopic and cosmic objects with the aid of the new powerful instruments will constitute one of the first tasks, and the morphological approach promises to become most useful and actually indispensable if we wish to succeed with a minimum expenditure of time and effort.

The Significance of Astronomy

In general neither the professional astronomers nor the laymen are clearly aware of the many practical applications of astronomy. A good view over this field can be gained if one begins to explore the following aspects:

1. What was the role played by astronomy in the spiritual life of the various historical periods?
2. What are the contributions of astronomy to the advancement of other sciences such as physics, chemistry, biology, medicine, history, archaeology and so on?
3. How did the results achieved by astronomers influence the course of technology and of life in general?
4. To what extent is the march into outer space made possible only because of the astronomical knowledge gained in the past?

THE CULTURAL IMPLICATIONS OF ASTRONOMY

As long as man knew only of the existence of his immediate surroundings, his outlook was severely restricted and the means for the development of his potentialities limited. As a result of insufficient knowledge he frequently fell prey to all sorts of superstitious beliefs and illusions. Such superstitions can have tragic consequences, as the history of the world proves again and again. Nothing could illustrate this better than the many unfortunate actions of the church, which in spite of the principles taught by the Bible concerning the dignity of man, is directly responsible for the ruthless slaughter of thousands upon thousands of men who often had done nothing more than recognize the true nature of the world long before the representatives of the church saw the daylight. Like the exploration of the world by the various discoverers and adventurers, as well as by the professional geographers and other scientists, the comprehensive survey and study of the celestial bodies and phenomena by astronomers has proved of the utmost importance for the recognition and elimination of paralysing superstitions and dogmas. True progress can be made only if all prejudices are eliminated. Thus, the way is opened towards the discovery, construction and practical application of all the new means for the realization of man's potential capabilities.

LIFE—AN UNIMAGINABLE MIRACLE

In the course of the astronomers' explorations of the universe the question naturally arose whether life on Earth is due to the a priori existence of unique and characteristic elements of matter or if it did evolve more or less accidentally from an intrinsically random combination of the elements of matter constituting the Earth's surface and the atmosphere at specific values of the pressures, temperatures, and intensity of the solar and cosmic radiation existing at that time. In this connection the now well-established fact impresses itself upon us that neither the Earth nor the Sun are at the center of the universe. In fact we have long ago abandoned the thought of such a center. This enormously heightens our desire to investigate and fully understand the role the local organic world and man himself play in the universe. Even before finding out whether or not we are the only living beings of our kind in the universe, however, it has become clear to us that life as we know it can exist only under certain very closely defined physico-chemical conditions, and its emergence on the Earth must be regarded as a truly astounding event. This knowledge of the intricate nature of living organisms must be regarded as one of the deepest insights gained by modern research.

THE INTERNATIONAL COMMUNITY OF ASTRONOMERS

Of great importance, philosophically and humanly, is the fact that among astronomers some of the most profound thinkers of all ages can be found. We recall the names of Aristarchus, Hipparchus, Copernicus, Galileo, Hale, and Lundmark. Occupation with the exciting celestial phenomena in the universe and the solitary work during thousands of lonely nights of observation obviously inspire universal minds to deep thought. As a gratifying result of such experiences great astronomers of all nations, whether they be democracies or not and regardless of their colour—black, yellow, brown, or white—form a remarkably close knit community and pursue essentially the same human goals. This was evidenced during the general assembly of the International Astronomical Union (IAU) in Berkeley, California, in August, 1961. On the one hand a sincere warning was sent to the government of the United States of America not to further pursue any irresponsible experimentation as a result of which extraterrestrial space or celestial bodies might become contaminated. Reference was made in particular to project Westford, which involved the launching of myriads of copper whiskers into a satellite orbit for the purpose of testing the reflection and scattering from them of radio waves. On the other hand we informed Mao Tse Tung that his request to expel the free Chinese Formosan astronomers from the IAU had been denied, and this decision had the support of all delegations, including those from the Communist countries.

As to the future prospects for a unified and sane world it is encouraging that the great astronomers of all countries form a group that spiritually and morally subscribes to the same principles. It will be our immediate task to bring to cooperate those among our colleagues who as yet do not seem to be interested in anything except promoting themselves. But even without them we must succeed in imbuing other internationally influential groups of men from all professions with the same desire for cooperation in all the great problems of the world.

ASTRONOMY AND ITS RELATION TO OTHER SCIENCES

Here we briefly sketch how astronomy through the ages influenced some of the other scientific disciplines. In the first place the observations made by astronomers concerning the distribution of the stars over the celestial sphere inspired the mathematicians to develop the methods of spherical geometry and trigonometry. On this basis it became possible to study the apparent motions of the Sun, the Moon, the planets, and the stars with astounding accuracy, and in the end it led Kepler to his crowning achievement, formulating his three famous laws on the motions of the then known planets in elliptical orbits with the Sun at one focus. In this connection the Babylonians should not be forgotten for their amazing feat of discovering the precession of the equinoxes with a period of about 26,000 years, which reflects the periodic motion of the terrestrial North and South Poles around the poles of the ecliptic, that is the intersections of the normal to the plane of the Earth's orbit with the celestial sphere. The laws of differential geometry and the tremendously important calculus of perturbations, that is, the method of successive approximations for the derivation of solutions of ever-increasing accuracy have occupied mathematicians from the time of Galileo until today. We mention in this connection only a few of the great names: E. Halley (1656–1742) who predicted the orbits of comets, including the famous Halley comet; L. Euler (theory of the perturbations of the planetary orbits, that is the deviations from the motions in exact ellipses); U. J. Leverrier (prediction of the existence and actual discovery of the planet Neptune on the basis of the perturbations observed in the orbit of the planet Uranus); and finally H. Poincaré ("mécanique céleste").

The Influence of Astronomy on Physics

The formulation of the laws of classical mechanics and gravitation by Galileo, Newton, and their great successors, among them Lagrange and Euler, was only possible through the analysis of astronomical observations on the basis of which the radically erroneous beliefs, entrenched during the two thousand years since Aristotle, could finally be dethroned. Physics is indebted to astronomy for numerous additional insights. A few examples may be mentioned. First, and we repeat, the fundamental laws of mechanics and those governing the long distance interactions of electrically neutral matter are to be credited in major part to astronomical research. The same is true for many aspects of the general theory of relativity. The original determination of the velocity of light as about 300,000 km/sec, a value that plays the central role in Einstein's special theory of relativity, is due to O. Roemer (1614–1710) who derived it from observations of the motion of the first moon of Jupiter. Only very much later did the physicists succeed in measuring this velocity in terrestrial laboratory experiments.

The behaviour of atoms and molecules at temperatures much higher than any which at that time could be reproduced in the laboratory was first analyzed through the observation of numerous absorption and emission lines, as they appear in the spectra of stars whose surface temperatures lie in the range from about 2000° to 100,000° Kelvin (or Celsius approximately). Furthermore some of the interstellar gaseous nebulae that are excited to fluorescence by the radiation from neighboring stars are so tenuous that certain spectral lines make their appearance, which on Earth could not be observed because even the best available vacuum pumps cannot sufficiently evacuate the gases from a given closed vessel to produce sufficiently low pressures. Observations of the so-called forbidden lines in celestial sources of exceedingly low material space density have furnished us with a tremendous wealth of new insights into the detailed characteristics of atoms, ions, molecules, and their excited states.

Furthermore, the study of the physics of the Earth's atmosphere has profited much from the results achieved through astronomical research. Much was learned for instance about turbulence, shock waves, and jet streams in the air from observations of the scintillations of the stars (twinkling of the stars). The analysis of the absorption and scattering of light passing through the atmosphere from the Sun and the stars furnished us with information about the composition and state of ionization of the various atoms and molecules in the different strata, while the coordination of the fluctuations in the intensity of the Earth's magnetic field with solar flares, Sun spots and other events on the Sun promises to give us important new clues to many of the intricate interrelations between numerous phenomena within the solar system.

Finally it should not be forgotten that the progress made in astronomy proved a constant inspiration to theoretical physics as well as to the applied physicists and engineers, who as a result invented and constructed many new instruments and devices for observation, testing, experimentation and analysis and reduction of data obtained in all fields of science and medicine. A few of these will be discussed later. Returning to the benefits theoretical physics enjoyed from astronomical research, the principal sources are in the fact that the astronomers discovered celestial objects on which many of the basic physical parameters, such as the density, the temperature, pressure, radiation intensity, gravitational potential, and the electromagnetic fields, may assume values surpassing those reproducible in the laboratory by many orders of magnitude. For instance, the average density of matter in a so-called white dwarf (Sirius B, the very faint companion of the bright star Sirius A is one of them) corresponds to about 100 kilograms per cubic centimeter. This observation provided the starting point for the theory of electronically degenerate matter. The consideration of this kind of matter further led to the conjecture that white dwarf stars under certain circumstances can shrink still further and collapse into neutron stars with densities of the order of 100 million tons per cubic centimeter and finally into hyperon stars, which reach the inconceivable limit of a billion tons of matter packed into the small space of one cubic centimeter.

Many similar examples might be cited, which show how astronomy had a beneficial influence on theoretical physics and chemistry.

Astronomy and Chemistry

Practical chemistry also profited much from astronomical research. Lockyer in 1868 had already discovered certain new spectral lines in the radiation from the sun, which in honour to this great spender of light he ascribed to a new and as yet unknown element, "helium." After this discovery, however, thirty years had to pass before Ramsay succeeded in isolating helium as well as the other noble gases neon, argon and so on, from available sources on the Earth.

A more intimate collaboration of the astronomers with the biologists and the physicians has just been initiated, especially by the three membership groups of the International Academy of Astronautics (IAA with headquarters in Paris) which comprise the exact sciences, the applied sciences, and engineering and the life sciences. Organizing efforts in this direction promise to become of the greatest importance in particular for the implementation of man's future space travels.

Astronomy and Archaeology

Archaeology has likewise made considerable use of the various results that have become available through research in astronomy. The exact knowledge of the positions and apparent motions of the Sun, the Moon, planets, comets and the stars has enabled archaeologists in many instances to derive essential clues for the deciphering of symbols representing the languages of ancient peoples. Nevertheless, enough fascinating problems remain to be solved concerning the written signs used for communication, for instance, those left by the Etruscans, Incas, Mayas, and other races.

Astronomical Research and Life in General

Although this is not immediately evident, and seldom properly appreciated, astronomical research has had an enormous influence on practical life. This includes the exploitation of astronomical knowledge by the common man, as well as the extensive use of many of the instruments and methods invented and developed by astronomers.

Navigation, the Calendar and the Clocks

The study of stellar configurations and their daily and yearly changes of apparent positions in the sky made navigation of the open seas possible as it was first achieved and practiced by the Polynesians and later by Columbus and all his millions of successors. Modern navigation, on the seas and through the air, of course makes use of the same astronomical knowledge, and space travel without it would be quite impossible. In the same context belong the establishment of a workable calendar, the invention of portable and reliable clocks and especially chronometers—the construction of which was suggested and insisted upon by the astronomers—and other achievements the universal importance of which need not be stressed any further.

The determination of the size of the Earth, starting from the first successful attempt by Eratosthenes (276–195 B.C.) until today, as well as the detailed survey of all the various localities on its surface, depend on exact observations of the relative positions of the stars with reference to landmarks on the surface of the Earth.

Instruments

Among the devices invented by astronomers the telescope and the portable clock are probably of the greatest importance. In war and in peace the refracting telescopes first invented by Galileo, and the reflecting telescopes initially constructed by Newton have found innumerable applications. In the future entirely new types of telescopes will become available, some of which will have a light-gathering power far beyond that of the present day instruments, while others will transform invisible radiations into visible light. Among these novel devices, which are already being used in a preliminary way, the photoelectronic telescope of Professor A. Lallemand in Paris is so far the most outstanding and successful. In this device, which was also independently invented and promoted by Dr. V. A. Zworykin, director of research for the Radio Corporation of America, and this author, light impinging on the focal surface is being transformed into electron beams, such that, after acceleration of the electrons through strong electric fields and magnetic refocusing, a tremendous enhancement of the original optical image is obtained. Astronomers therefore expect that photoelectronic devices of small apertures and light weight will eventually outperform the giant 200-inch Hale reflector on Palomar Mountain. In any case these new instruments will be indispensable if we intend seriously to explore the universe with the aid of rocket-borne instrumentation.

ASTRONOMICAL RESEARCH CAN BE CONDUCTED AND ENJOYED BY ALL

As we have previously stated, the work of astronomers has yielded results in many auxiliary fields, such as that of the photographic emulsions, the construction of optical gratings, photocells, bolometers, radiometers, radiotelescopes, and so on, the use of which has proved fruitful in all fields of science and practical technology. It is, however, not possible in this book to go into any more details, since the book's principal purpose is to give short morphological surveys and inspire the reader to proceed further on his own.

Before closing I wish to emphasize that in my opinion astronomy is a science in which everybody can actively participate and actually hope to make valuable contributions. In fact, in explaining the principles of astronomical research to laymen, one can easily demonstrate to them that they can constructively collaborate in discovery, invention and research. At the present time astronomy is perhaps the science in which such discoveries and inventions can be made most easily, and many useful instruments and methods of observation and reduction can be developed and applied even by outsiders. I do not think that I am exaggerating when I state that astronomy is more easily accessible to everybody than any other science. I therefore suggest that some of those who have enough leisure time and have retired from active professional life have a try at it and demonstrate as amateur astronomers that the world may well be brought into better balance through the close cooperation of laymen with the professional men of research.

The most important achievement of astronomy is to have opened up horizons to the human mind enormously greater than those commonly visualized by its sister sciences and to have before all eliminated one superstitious belief about the universe after another. Following the work of the greatest among the astronomers, equally universal minds among the representatives of the other sciences will no doubt endeavour to rid themselves of all limited horizons and collaborate in the most urgent task of ridding the human mind from all of its pathological aberrations, a task which must be considered as the ultimate goal of all research.

Recommended Literature

Amateur Telescope Making, New York, The Scientific American Publishing Co.

Advanced Telescope Making, New York, The Scientific American Publishing Co.

P. Couderc: *l'Astrologie*, Paris, Presses Universitaires, 1951.

E. Zinner: *Astronomie. Geschichte ihrer Probleme*, Freiburg I. B., K. Alber Verlag, 1951.

E. Zinner: *Die Geschichte der Sternkunde*, Berlin, J. Springer Verlag, 1931.

L. Motz and A. Duveen: *Essentials of Astronomy*, Belmont California, Wadsworth Publishing Co., 1966.

F. Zwicky, *Morphological Astronomy*, Berlin, J. Springer Verlag, 1957.

8

Special Applications
of the Morphological Approach III:
The March into the Universe

Most of our information on the cosmic bodies and phenomena was obtained during the past five thousand years from observations made from the surface of the Earth without or with instruments. These observations were analyzed by the astronomers and physicists on the basis of knowledge gained from terrestrial laboratory experiments. Our march into the universe until very recently was therefore a purely imaginary one and consisted entirely of a complex of interpretations of observational data. As was described in the previous chapter, one of the principal results derived from these studies was the knowledge that the part of the cosmic space that can be explored with the largest present day telescopes is populated everywhere by stars, galaxies and clusters of galaxies of the same general structure, physical characteristics and chemical composition, and that their distribution is essentially random and uniform. Only the occurrence of organic and conscious life may possibly be more localized. There exist so far no indications that life as we know it also exists on other celestial objects. More light on this question may be shed in the near future, since today we are at the beginning of active space research, and we now dispose of entirely new means of exploration such as rocket-borne tele-

scopes and preliminary observing stations on the Moon. In contradistinction to classical astronomy the new astronomy will not
any longer be earthbound and the following avenues may be
followed:

1. Observations of the happenings in the universe with instruments mounted in extraterrestrial locations.

2. The new astronomy will be in a position to investigate the
various members of the solar system in direct contact.

3. Man himself will travel into interplanetary space and settle
on the Moon and the planets, which will be partly "recon-
structed" for the purpose of further developing our inherent
potentialities and enriching our lives.

4. If man endures long enough, attempts will, no doubt,
eventually be made to accelerate the Sun to a sufficiently high
velocity to allow it to reach the immediate neighborhood of one
of the nearest stars, say Alpha Centauri within the life span
of a few dozen generations (see pp. 153–54). How such a feat
might be accomplished will be discussed later.

5. In order not to blunder into space as we have blundered
into so many large-scale new projects and developments, many
more men of research will have to acquire a new universal
outlook and start to collaborate with the common man in
the common cause for a unified world, as we suggested it in
the first chapter.

The reader who may be shaking his head about the plans proposed above and about the author's optimism in the wake of continued disappointments should nevertheless be reminded of the
fact that those among us pioneers who twenty-five years ago
promoted and initiated the construction of giant rockets for space
travel were not considered quite sane at that time—an attitude
that later on had a devastating influence on the standing among
the neutral peoples watching the relative achievements of the
Russians and the Americans in rocketry.

Observations From Extraterrestrial Locations

Except for visual light in the wavelength range from three
thousand to seven thousand Angstroms (one Angstrom = 10^{-7}

mm) and radio waves from about one centimeter to thirty meters wavelength, the atmosphere absorbs practically all other electromagnetic radiations that come to us from the various self-luminous celestial bodies. The same is true for the corpuscular rays from outer space except for the most energetic cosmic rays, which at least partly succeed in passing through the atmosphere and the Earth's magnetic field. In order to observe all the radiations from cosmic space, it was therefore necessary to send telescopes, ionization chambers, Geiger counters, and other recording devices high up into the tenuous strata of the upper atmosphere, first with the aid of balloons and later, since 1946, with sounding rockets. The first flights launched in 1908 by the Swiss physicist Professor Albert Gockel had already showed that not only light but cosmic rays, that is corpuscular radiations, likewise impinge on the upper atmosphere from outer space. These latter contain in particular most energetic and preponderantly electrically charged elementary particles of matter, which ionize the molecules of the atmosphere and thus constantly produce electric charges. The story of the investigation of the cosmic rays is a long and most interesting one inasmuch as during the past forty years hypotheses and theories were advanced by many of the very best physicists, which one after another proved to be completely false. As a result of innumerable balloon flights and an immense amount of work it was finally ascertained that cosmic rays contain protons (the nuclei of hydrogen atoms) as well as the nuclei of most of the heavier elements, which may possess individual energies of up to a hundred billion billion (10^{20}) electron volts. (One electron volt is the kinetic energy an electron acquires when falling through an electric potential difference of one volt.) For comparison it should be remembered that the giant proton accelerator of the European Cooperative for Nuclear Research (Cern) in Geneva, Switzerland, with its ring channel of 200 meters in diameter, produces protons of 28 billion electron volts (28×10^9 eV).

Although the discussions concerning the origin of the cosmic rays still continue at a lively pace, it may not be stated with considerable confidence that a great fraction of the most energetic particles is produced in supernova outbursts, a hypothesis which was first advanced by the author in 1933.

Balloons, which may reach a height of 40 kilometers with payloads of 100 kg, are also most useful for carrying instrumentation for the recording of infrared radiations from various celestial sources. In the lower atmosphere these rays are absorbed by the water vapour present, which is absent in the upper strata.

Until recently, however, little work has been done in the infrared range of wavelengths, since no sensitive recording instruments were available. This deficiency has now been largely removed through developments in the physics of the solid state, and there is hope that experiments and observations in progress will give us information on extraterrestrial long wave radiations and with it on the concentration in interstellar space of as yet unobserved constituents, such as molecular hydrogen. It is furthermore probable that certain infrared rays are not being unduly absorbed or scattered by the interstellar dust clouds, and that we shall therefore succeed in exploring not only the central parts of our galaxy,* but also be able to observe extragalactic stellar systems, which in the visible range of light are blotted out by interstellar obscuration.

For the observation of ultraviolet light from the stars, balloon flights are of little use because the atmosphere is opaque for these wavelengths to heights of over one hundred kilometers. The first successes in the analysis of the ultraviolet spectrum of the Sun were thus achieved through the use of instruments sent aloft on captured German V-2 rockets from White Sands (New Mexico) Proving Grounds and later by the very excellent Aerobee rockets of the Aerojet General Corporation in Azusa.

Observations of the kind mentioned have unfortunately been very costly so far, since many rockets were needed and valuable instruments could not be recovered but were destroyed on their return to Earth. Present projects by the United States National

---

* This statement, which I made three years ago when writing the German edition of this book, has already been confirmed; see E. Becklin and G. Neugebauer, "Infrared Observations of the Galactic Center," *Astr. J.* 72.292 (1967).

Aeronautics and Space Administration (NASA), therefore, propose the use of "orbiting astronomical observatories," that is telescopes mounted on artificial satellites circling the Earth for long periods of time. The greatest breakthrough is naturally expected to occur once observatories can be established on the Moon. Seen from that basis, the sky in all directions is always "dark," except if one looks in the direction of the sun, the zodiacal light, or any of the other extended weak sources of light. Astronomers on the Moon will be able to work around the clock if their personal state of health and the labor unions will allow them to do so. With telescopes in extraterrestrial locations astronomers expect in particular to collect significant data, which will allow them to liquidate some of the long-standing problems concerning the size, age and evolution of the universe and its material and phenomenological contents.

Experiments with Extraterrestrial Matter

So far our knowledge of the constitution of celestial bodies rests solely on intricate conclusions drawn from observations. Only recently have we started on rudimentary types of direct experimentation, which in principle are the following:

1. Light rays or radio waves generated by emitters on the Earth may be sent into outer space and their reflection or scattering from various celestial objects observed.

2. Ultrafast particles can be launched from the Earth or from space capsules, and their impacts on the Moon, the planets and the Sun observed. Rockets can, in addition, carry sounding devices to the extraterrestrial bodies and relay the information gathered, back to the Earth.

3. Finally man can fly into outer space himself and conduct his experiments on location.

How fast progress is being made is obvious from the fact that since the preceding paragraphs were written a few years ago, for inclusion in the original German edition of this book, several of the goals described have already been achieved by means of space vehicles launched both from the United States of America (Ranger, Surveyor, Mariner) and by the Russians.

All the three types of projects described above were planned and initiated twenty-five years ago. At that time the first radar beams were directed against the Moon, which reflected them, so that on their return two and one half seconds later they were recorded and analyzed. This procedure yielded important information on the physical properties of the surface of the Moon. After the invention of the so-called "Masers," that is recording instruments of extraordinary sensitivity, the electronics engineers of the California Institute of Technology succeeded in 1962 in sending radar signals to the planet Venus and recording their reflection back to the Earth. These experiments permitted the determination of the distance of Venus and the Sun from the Earth with an accuracy of better than plus or minus 1,000 kilometers in a total of 150 million kilometers. This accuracy is about one hundred times greater than that which could previously be achieved through the best conventional methods available to astronomers. Most recently the "Lasers" have been invented and constructed, that is, devices that can generate almost monochromatic and directed visual light rays of great intensity. With such laser beams small areas of the Moon can be illuminated, and their albedo (degree of reflectivity) measured in dependence upon wavelength. Such observations allow us to draw important conclusions about the nature of the reflecting surfaces of the various members of the planetary system.

In 1946 the author made a first attempt at launching artificial meteors with velocities of more than 11.2 km/sec (the escape velocity from the Earth) into interplanetary space. These particles were produced as jets from exploding "hollow charges" mounted on a V-2 rocket. The first experiment at the White Sands Proving Grounds on December 17, 1946, failed for quite accidental reasons. Unfortunately we did not succeed during the next eleven years in mobilizing sufficient support for a repetition of our experiments. We thus had to wait until the night of October 16, 1957, at which time we finally launched an artificial meteor, weighing about two grams, with a velocity of 15 km/sec from an Aerobee rocket at a height of 90 kilometers into space, free from the gravitational pull of the Earth. Since this event took place twelve days after the launching of Sputnik I, the world heard little about our success. We subsequently tried in vain to obtain funds and the official permission to shoot directly at the Moon. The impact of a small ultrafast particle on the Moon could have been observed with one of the giant reflecting telescopes and would have allowed us to obtain information about the chemical composition of its surface that would have been of the greatest importance in the preparations for launching men and instruments to the Moon. Such information is still lacking, especially since the Russian Lunik II hit the surface of the Moon at a time of the day that made it impossible for us at the Palomar Observatory to train the 200-inch telescope on it, and also because, for unknown reasons, the astronomers on the east coast of the United States and our colleagues in Europe failed to make any observations. Later on American and Russian Moon rockets produced many photographic records of the Moon's surface, but no information about the immediate layers just below it. For this reason it is to be urgently recommended that suitable projectiles be shot against the surface of the Moon from spacecraft that circle or approach it and that observations of the resulting flashes and the ejected dust clouds be made either from the Earth or from the space capsules themselves.

Twenty years have now passed since we attempted on December 17, 1946, at White Sands Proving Grounds to start the march into the universe in earnest. For the occasion, Dr. A. G. Wilson, associate director at the Douglas Advanced Research Laboratory in Huntington Beach, California, has written an article entitled "The Anniversary of a Historic Failure," which appeared in *Engineering and Science* magazine, published by the California Institute of Technology in December, 1966, and is here reproduced:

The pages of *Engineering and Science* magazine provide a

historical record of many of the achievements and successes of Caltech researchers—alumni and staff. The dead ends and failures rarely appear in print. Fortunately for publication costs, few people want their failures recorded. However, now and then certain types of failures become historic and deserve a place in the record.

The 17th of December this year marks the 20th anniversary of such a historic failure—the first attempt to launch particles into space with escape velocity. A team of Caltech men headed by Fritz Zwicky, professor of astronomy, in cooperation with Army Ordnance, the Johns Hopkins Applied Physics Laboratory, the Harvard College Observatory, and the New Mexico School of Mines, put together a project in White Sands, New Mexico, combining the hardware components available in 1946 in a way which, theoretically, would launch a few pellets in orbit about the earth or throw them off into interplanetary space. Two marginal devices and one valid motivation made the attempt worthwhile. The devices were the V-2 rocket and the Monroe rifle grenade or "shaped charge." The motivation was to generate a shower of artificial meteors in order to calibrate the luminous efficiency of natural meteors.

The possibility of throwing something up that would not come down again fired the imagination. Although there had been 16 postwar V-2 rocket firings, this was to be the first night firing of a V-2 in the United States. In those days the launching of a V-2, with or without an instrument on board, was as much news as the launching of a Gemini today. Dr. Zwicky, who designed the experiment, placed the event in historical context: "We first throw a little something into the skies, then a little more, then a shipload of instruments—then ourselves."

A V-2 rocket was equipped with six 150-gram penolite shaped charges with 30-gram steel inserts. These were set to fire at times after launching that would eject the slugs of molten steel at heights of approximately 50, 65, and 75 kilometers. At these heights the ejection velocities of from 10 to 15 km/sec would place the slugs either in orbit or on escape trajectory. The ultimate fate of a slug would depend on its mass and velocity. Most would be meteors, but some might not be consumed.

To determine the destinies of the meteors, a battery of K4 aerial cameras equipped with rotating shutters was scattered over the White Sands Proving Range. One of these was equipped with a transparent objective grating to obtain spectra of the V-2 exhaust jet and the luminous artificial meteors launched. The sites were selected to acquire optimal triangulation data. In addition the Caltech eight-inch Schmidt camera was removed from its usual house at Palomar and set up a few miles south of the launch site to photograph the flight of the V-2 rocket and of the particles ejected from the shaped charges. Astronomers at nearby observatories with wide angle telescopes also focused in on the firing.

As this 17th postwar V-2 left the pad at 22^h 12^m 49^s mountain standard time, expectations were high. There was a feeling that history was being made. There was also the anxiety that has become as much part of every launching as the countdown. (The 16th rocket, fired a few days earlier, had tilted on lift-off and travelled 131 miles horizontally.) Lifting slowly, No. 17 filled the whole range with sound and, falling upward, held true to its course—5° tilt north. The shutters clicked and telescopes tracked—then burnout. But the rocket could still be followed by the red glow from its exhaust vanes. The time came and passed for the three pairs of charge detonations. Nothing was seen. The rocket mounted to a new record of 114 miles, then returned to earth.

Films were hastily developed in hope of seeing on the emulsion what could not be seen in the sky. But there were no trails. Tests of the charges made on previous evenings had been in every way successful. Had the charges fired, but been undetected? Subsequent investigations have not solved the mystery of just what did happen.

Just as man's first attempts at flight in the atmosphere failed, the first attempt to reach space with a chance of succeeding also failed. It is significant, however, that whereas the span between the first attempts to fly and the first successful flight is measured in centuries, the span between the first attempt to achieve orbital velocity and the successful orbiting of Sputnik was only one decade. Those who participated directly and indirectly in this experiment, though failing to launch the space age on the night of December 17, 1946, have to their credit an important contribution leading to later triumphs. Zwicky's idea was ultimately vindicated, when success crowned the *second* experimental firing of shaped charges from a rocket on October 16, 1957—twelve days after the Russians launched Sputnik.

The press in 1946 reacted favourably to our project of starting the March into Space. A most characteristic comment was written by E. B. White in *The New Yorker*, December 27, 1946. This piece, which later was included in his book *The Second Tree from the Corner* on pages 126 and 127, is herewith quoted with the permission of Harper and Row, Publishers, New York.

Experimentation, by E. B. White

The year ends on a note of pure experimentation. Dr. Fritz Zwicky last week tried to hurl some metal slugs out into space free of the Earth's gravitational pull. Dr. Zwicky stood in New Mexico and tossed from there. He was well equipped: he had a rocket that took the slugs for the first forty mile leg of the journey and then discharged them at high velocity to continue on their own. The desire to toss something in a new way, or to toss it at a greater distance, is fairly steady in men and boys. Boys stand on high bridges, chucking chips down wind, or they stand on the shore of a pond, tossing rocks endlessly at a floating bottle, or at a dead cat, observing closely every detail of their experiment, trying to make every stone sail free of the pull of past experience. Then the boys grow older, stand in the desert, still chucking, observing, wondering. They have almost exhausted the Earth's possibilities and are going on into the empyrean to throw at the stars, leaving the Earth's people frightened and joyless, and leaving some fellow scientists switching over from science to politics and hoping they have made the switch in time.

Man's Journey to the Moon and the Planets

As a first stage of our march into space we shall no doubt try to land men on the Moon and have them install themselves there. This can be accomplished in many ways. Since I know my own plan best, and since it was probably the first one to be proposed seriously, it is here briefly sketched. The chief point of this plan is that the astronauts carry with them special equipment that will allow them to use the Sun's radiation for the processing of some of the rocks on the Moon's surface, for the purpose of producing the following necessities of life:

1. Walls must be erected immediately that protect the astronauts against the radiation from the Sun and the corpuscular rays sporadically ejected from it.

2. Gaseous oxygen mixed with nitrogen must be generated, since pure oxygen alone, for as yet unknown reasons is not suitable for continued breathing.

3. Water must be generated out of the rocks.

4. Continually operating mechanical and electrical power supplies must be installed.

5. It would also be most desirable to produce propellants suitable for local vehicles and for rockets to return to the Earth.

6. Food must be synthesized from the elements extracted from the Moon's surface.

All of the above-mentioned requirements can be met through the installation of good solar furnaces, which will process the materials available on the Moon's surface, as shown in Figure 28. These materials might have to be brought up from a depth of several meters if the surface layers should have lost their crystal water and CO_2 because of continued bombardment by the cosmic

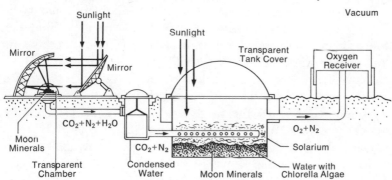

Fig. 28. *Installation for Sustenance of Life on the Moon: Sunlight is concentrated (focused) on the moon minerals in a vacuum-tight, transparent bell jar by a mirror combination. Water of crystallization (H_2O), carbon dioxide (CO_2), and nitrogen (N_2) are liberated from the minerals through the resulting intense heating and are conducted into the watery suspension of chlorella algae in the "lunar garden" shown. Drinking water is also condensed in this container. The algae, with the aid of sunlight, "digest" the carbon dioxide and exude oxygen which, together with nitrogen and some remaining carbon dioxide, is collected in the tank at the right for breathing and other purposes.*

rays. It is estimated that the whole equipment to be carried along from the Earth might weigh a few hundred kilograms. The collecting mirrors for the solar furnaces should have a size of several square meters, but they need not be really very perfect. As to suitable installations for sustaining life on Mars and Venus, no adequate plans can be made until more information becomes available on the physical conditions that prevail on their surfaces. At the present time this information is still very scanty, but it may soon be obtained from Mariner IV, which has just been launched (in June, 1967) and a Russian exploring rocket preceding it by two days.

Journeys to the Nearest Stars In the Tow of the Sun

For the purpose of traveling to the nearest stars, Alpha Centauri for instance, at a distance of four light years, rockets do not suffice. A very much more exciting possibility offers itself, however: We remain on the Earth and travel with it as the space vehicle, either alone or with the whole solar system towards our goal. During this journey we may enjoy and use the light from the Sun as always, or if we wish to leave it behind, we can keep warm and provide all of the necessary small and large-scale illumination through the proper use of nuclear fusion energy. Traveling at a speed of 500 km/sec through space, relative to the surrounding stars, we might reach the neighborhood of Alpha Centauri in about 2,500 years. All of this will become possible once we have mastered nuclear fusion ignition of common materials on the Earth and on the Sun. Physicists in many countries have been attempting during the past fifteen years to induce nuclear fusion reactions in extremely concentrated and high-energy ionic plasmas, without making any use of the release of nuclear fission energy from uranium as it is being used in H-bombs. Even if these efforts should be successful they would not provide us with any readily usable means for the acceleration of the Sun or of the Earth to velocities of the order of 500 km/sec. I have therefore suggested another approach striving to produce small solid particles with velocities of up to 1,000 km/sec. It is not possible here to go into any details of how this is going to be done. I emphasize only that no fundamental difficulties stand in the way. Particles impacting on dense matter with velocities of the order of 1,000 km/sec will generate the desired temperatures of hundreds of millions of degrees, at which all light elements will be ignited to nuclear fusion reactions.

Launching ultrafast particles against the Sun, local regions on it could be ignited to nuclear fusion. As a consequence of the tremendous release of energy by such reactions, matter would be ejected with velocities of the order of 50,000 km/sec, while the resulting forces of reaction would propel the Sun in the opposite direction. If such processes were applied for a long time, the Sun could eventually be accelerated to the desired velocity with a sacrifice of only a small per cent of its total mass.

Since the planets are held in rein by the Sun's gravitational field, they and the Earth would be carried along on the distant journey. In principle the process and propulsion described could be applied to the Earth alone, which then would detach itself from the solar system and start out on its solitary voyage to the nearest stars.

Purpose of the March Into the Universe

Many have asked the question about what the march into the universe is good for and which goals should be pursued in particular. While the Russians, except for innocuous statements, have officially said nothing about the issues involved, a tremendous controversy and confusion has arisen in the United States concerning the significance of space travel and space research. The following considerations may help in clarifying the complex circumstances and problems involved.

1. Physicists, chemists, biologists, and physicians intend to make observations in space that are impossible on the Earth. Furthermore, experiments can be conducted in the empty and essentially gravitation-free space that cannot be reproduced on

the Earth. As an example, the artificial growth of perfect single crystals promises to become of the greatest importance both for the advancement of theoretical physics and astronomy as well as for numerous practical applications. Furthermore it will be of vital interest to conduct experiments on the behaviour of the elementary building stones of living organisms in sterile and practically weight-free space.

2. Numerous observations and experiments, which in principle are possible on the Earth, can be carried out much more easily and economically in extraterrestrial locations.

3. Concerning the safeguarding of our existence and the military implications for the tragic confrontations of nations and peoples of different creeds and races, the psychological and material gains to be reaped as a result of the successful mastery of means of travel into outer space must be seriously considered.

4. As among mountain climbers or comrades in arms in actual combat, close ties seem to exist and to be formed among the men who collaborate in the preparation and the execution of the march into space. Such human bonds unfortunately are disappearing more and more. It is therefore to be hoped that the great tasks which lie before us in the exploration of outer and inner space will inspire men of research, engineers, physicians, professionals from all fields, and the common man of all nations to collaborate ever more intimately. It should be emphasized again that historians, lawyers, and enlightened politicians and statesmen in particular have realized for some time that we must not blunder into the space age as we have bungled many of the great projects before, if we are to survive. The most farsighted astronomers share this conviction, although too many of their colleagues are still exclusively self-centered or are interested only in special and often irresponsible projects as a result of whose realization the Earth's surface and atmosphere, as well as the whole planetary system, might become contaminated in many ways which could impede research or render it downright impossible.

The jurists, practicing lawyers, scientists, and physicians of the International Academy of Astronautics in particular are making all efforts to bring their colleagues, and beyond that, all peoples on Earth to their senses and have them not only agree to a peaceful treaty regulating our exploration and exploitation of outer and inner space but also collaborate in the common efforts for the purpose of the evolution and enrichment of all human life.

Integral Outlook

Most laymen seem to think that the problems that need to be solved to enable us to travel to the Moon and the planets are the most difficult as yet encountered by man. This, however, is not actually the case. Those who are in the know regarding the requirements for the march into space are well aware of the fact that this project does not involve any fundamental technical difficulties or any particular ingenuity. Only a very conscientious and massive effort is needed to insure success. On the other hand it will be very much more difficult to explore all the characteristics of the elements constituting living organisms, as contrasted with the building stones of inanimate matter, and to deal efficiently with such problems as the conquering of cancer and other deadly diseases. And most urgent of all, the greatest ingenuity will have to be mobilized to recognize the true nature of the various aberrations of the human mind and to discover means for their sublimation and elimination. As was stressed previously, the overcoming of the aberrations and superstitions, and prejudices and dogmas originating from them represent the ultimate goals of every universal man of research and true scholar who is interested not only in studying this or that special phenomenon, but who never loses sight of the most fundamental values in life.

In conclusion it should be pointed out that, unfortunately, the countries of central Europe, Germany, Austria, and Switzerland in particular, have not kept pace with the necessary preparations for space travel and space research, although they are technically among the strongest and have actually pioneered in the development of modern rockets, gas turbines and sophisticated instrumentation. All the scientific disciplines are involved in the work for the exploration of outer space, and all of them can profit materially by participating in it. Considering the technical and spiritual potentials of the countries mentioned, as well as those of other peoples, it is of the greatest importance for the safeguarding of their existence and the maintenance of their high standards of life that they recover as soon as possible what they have lost, in order to allow them to make their proper and significant contribution towards the stabilization of all the constructive interrelations, both technical and human, of the various parts of the world.

Recommended Literature

A. C. Clarke, *Interplanetary Flight*, New York, Harper and Row, Publishers, 1962.

Space Age Astronomy, (Symposium of the International Astronomical Union, Pasadena, California, August, 1961). Academic Press, Inc., New York and London 1962.

F. Zwicky. *Morphology of Propulsive Power*, Monograph No. 1 of the Society for Morphological Research, Pasadena, Calif., 1962.

9

Review and Preview: Epitomy of Morphological Thought and Action

In conclusion, the intrinsic aspects of the morphological out-look and the morphological mode of life will be reviewed once more. It has occasionally been said that morphological research and constructive action are not new; this has been stated in particular by some of those who are themselves quite incapable of creating anything new and who actually could not successfully have dealt with many of the problems which have already been solved with the aid of the morphological approach. Furthermore, some scientists have claimed that morphological research is identical with good science. This, however, is by no means true, as follows from the fact that excellent science has been done off and on for many centuries, but in spite of the resulting achievements the world has remained afflicted with exceedingly serious ills, which could have been eliminated long ago if scientists had used their knowledge conscientiously and uncompromisingly for that purpose, instead of pursuing their own selfish ends. We are actually forced to conclude that scientists are either quite incapable of dealing with certain of the most important human problems or they show no desire to do so. In fact, physicists are generally only interested in physics, mathematicians in mathematics, astronomers, chemists, biologists and others only in astronomy, chemistry, biology and so on. The morphologist on the other hand not only deals with the special aspects and the interrelations in one individual discipline, but also with the integral relations among them. And before all, morphological research is concerned with the evaluation of the possible applications of all sciences to the world in general and to humanity in particular, projects which it aims to realize and to control for the purpose of the achievement of optimum goals and values.

In elucidation of what has just been said, a few typical examples will be mentioned.

The great mathematicians of the seventeenth century were concerned with the interesting problem of determining the shape of the frictionless sliding surface on which a point mass would move in the shortest possible time from a point A to a lower point B, not situated directly vertically under A. Johann Bernoulli (1667–1748) proved by a most ingenious method that this curve, called the brachistochrone is a cycloid. In this case, brilliant scientific, but in no way morphological, thinking produced the desired solution. Johann's brother Jakob Bernoulli (1654–1705) and in particular the great mathematician Leonhard Euler (1707–83) recognized later that the problem of the brachistochrone represents a special case of a very rich class of so-called extremum problems, which are concerned with the search for the absolute minima of certain mathematical functions depending on many variables. This type of general outlook, which may be called morphological science, resulted in the development of the theory of variations and subsequently led to most important advances in mathematics, analytical mechanics, astronomy, physics, and chemistry. It should be emphasized, however, that a professional morphologist would ascribe to morphological science a still wider meaning. He would not be satisfied with the theory of variations as being the only possible general solution of extremum problems of the type described. He would, in addition, insist upon the search for all possible methods with which such problems could be solved. But even morphological science so understood is by no means of the universality and objectivity visualized by the morphological approach. For the unprejudiced morphologist all relations and all implications of the achievements of scientific research about the manyfold material and spiritual manifestations of life are of the utmost interest and importance. In this sense the morphological outlook reaches far beyond conventional science. In this connection attention should be called to some of my predecessors in science and philosophy who must have had similar thoughts in mind. I mention only Paracelsus (1493?–1541), P. L. M. de Maupertuis (1698–1759), J. J. Bachofen (1815–87), and Fridtjof Nansen (1861–1930).

In the engineering sciences we can find analogous examples that illustrate how initially restricted results were expanded and led to ever more general technical and sociological developments. Invention and construction of specific devices were followed by the occupation with whole classes of engines and instruments, which finally were produced for optimum use by the whole of human society and for the remodeling of many of the unsatisfactory features of the external world and the introduction of entirely new ones.

The invention and construction of the Diesel engine, the axial compressor and the gas turbine by Rudolph Diesel (1858–1913) and A. Stodola (1859–1942) are no doubt first-class technical achievements. But neither Diesel nor my one-time teacher and old friend Professor Stodola of the Federal Institute of Technology in Zurich, Switzerland, were engineer morphologists in the sense that they did not stop at their specific successes but continued uncompromisingly and systematically to visualize and promote the realization of the *totality of all possible thermal power plants*. This remained as a much more general task to be accomplished by the theoreticians and practitioners of modern morphological research.* In all justice it must be said, however, that Stodola in some ways had a presentiment of what was to come, as

---

* F. Zwicky, *Morphology of Propulsive Power*, Monograph No. 1 of the Society for Morphological Research, Pasadena, 1962.

he clearly presented it in the profound epilogue to his classical book on steam and gas turbines.*

The exploration and analysis of all of the interrelations that exist among whole classes of material objects, as well as among groups of phenomena, ideas and concepts, set goals of a scope that lies far beyond those of present day science. To make progress towards these goals morphologists must be capable of the utmost unbias, that is detachment from all prejudice, and they must possess power of decision and indomitable courage such as unfortunately are rarely found among present day scientists. In support of this statement a few trivial examples may be cited which illustrate that the much-praised universal outlook and unbias of science are largely a myth.

For instance, as is well known to the general public, there are available for "distribution" to the men of research and to scholars, numerous kudos, such as prizes, medals, honorary degrees, and positions. Morphologists have justly raised the question, would science not be better off and progress more rapid without the bestowal of such formal signs of recognition to individuals and collective achievements? In other words, would it not be preferable if every scientist were known to the world for what he has accomplished and for our confidence in him for what he still might achieve in the future? To ask questions of this sort, however, is essentially taboo today. Most of the scientists apparently prefer, probably not all of them for unselfish reasons, to play the games of favoritism, patronage, collusion, and nepotism with prizes, stipends, medals, and promotions, to form cliques, pressure groups, and "mutual admiration societies," and to forgo independence in order to concentrate the desired powers in their hands and retain it as long as possible. Otherwise competent and unbiased lone wolves might raise havoc with their cherished ways of life.

The morphologist can only suggest that one at least attempt to tabulate achievements in science as objectively as possible to prevent the plagiarists and thieves from walking away with the

---

* A. Stodola, *Dampf-und Gasturbinen*, 6th edition, Berlin, 1925.

laurels. Thus some deserving colleagues may at least be given a small chance. In astronomy one might ask who invented a certain type of telescope, who first built it, put it in successful operation, and what were the most important results achieved through its use. One would also search the records for those who predicted the existence of various types of stars and galaxies and who did the most important observational work in the respective fields. Furthermore an objective tabulation would list the names of the men who started and developed radio, X-ray and balloon astronomy, work with instrumented rockets, and so on. One might further evaluate the usually little-appreciated but generally excruciating efforts of those who laid the groundwork for so many of the later researches through their extended observational surveys and the compilation of data gathered in the construction of comprehensive catalogues. The results of such objective surveys of efforts and achievements could be made available periodically to the whole scientific community. All interested would be free to express their opinions, adding and subtracting from the original preliminary evaluations. Foundations, academies, scientific societies as well as publishers would then have the choice of accepting or ignoring the results of such polls, their decisions showing good or bad judgment, as the case might be.

A further evil, which sorely ails present day science, has its origin in the entrenched habit of many of the leading technical journals, with those in the United States at the helm, of having all papers that are submitted reviewed by critics unknown to the authors. To my knowledge few of these critics have ever had the courtesy or the decency to divulge their identity. As a consequence there is much malicious shooting from ambush being practiced, and too often fundamental contributions have been suppressed or their publication interminably postponed through the simple subterfuge of requesting the author repeatedly to introduce irrelevant alterations. Anonymous referees are thus safe in their doings since they cannot later on be confronted with the consequences wrought and held to account for their criticisms which, as it happened all too often, were unjustified and had a devastating or destructive influence on the progress not only of science but also on the fortunes of the human society as a whole.

In this connection it is of interest to call the attention of the public to the following significant facts: The Association of American Universities has officially adopted a set of principles,* one of which states that all faculty members may submit for publication all results of their research and their thoughts without being interfered with or censored in any way or manner by their universities. In spite of this, off and on one of the institutions involved, in violation of the tenets just stated, appoints a committee (packed court) to act as censors of what should or should not be published. There are numerous regrettable instances to be cited in support of the statements just made about this practice. Since I naturally know my own experiences best, some of them are submitted here. I must stress, however, that many of my colleagues have fared even worse, inasmuch as they have been deprived of merited recognition for important discoveries and achievements because of impeding tactics of hierarchically and far from impartially conducted editing practices of scientific journals, as a consequence of whose machinations the recognition and the rewards for their work were cynically gathered in by plain plagiarists.

In 1945, as a neutral expert fluent in several languages, I was commissioned by the United States Air Force to investigate the remarkable achievements made by the German scientists and engineers in the invention, construction and practical operation of small and large-scale rockets of all kinds. (see F. Zwicky, *Report on Certain Phases of War Research in Germany*, 188 pages, Wright Field, Ohio, 1947). Upon my return to California I proposed to start using some of the captured V-rockets for the exploration of the upper atmosphere and extraterrestrial space, as well as to build special carriers (Aerobee rockets) of instrumentation for the purpose. My first scientific contribution in this field, an article on the possibility of earth-launched artificial meteors for direct ex-

---

* *The Rights and Responsibilities of Universities and Their Faculties*. A statement by the Association of American Universities, adopted March 24, 1953. Issued by the Princeton University, Princeton, N.J.

perimentation with the constituents of the upper atmosphere and the various objects of the solar system was rejected by the *Physical Review*. This leading journal and official organ of the American Physical Society wrote me that they were not interested in any ideas and proposals of projects about any future space research. My paper, however, was subsequently accepted for publication by the *Publications of the Astronomical Society of the Pacific* (Vol. 58, p. 260, 1946, and Vol. 59, p. 32, 1947). Although my first experiments on December 17, 1946, failed, I eventually succeeded on October 16, 1957, in launching the first man-made object into interplanetary space free from the gravitational pull of the Earth, as I had predicted in 1946 (see pp. 234–38 and my article "The First Shot Into Interplanetary Space," *Engineering and Science Journal*, California Institute of Technology, January, 1958), thus contributing towards the initiation of the subsequent large-scale preparations for space research and man's march into the universe.

In the early 1930's I concluded on the basis of some fundamental theoretical considerations that intergalactic space between the many stellar systems cannot be completely empty. As expected from the theory, the observational search for small intergalactic swarms of stars and for gas and dust clouds in the vast spaces between the known bright galaxies proved eminently successful. My results, however, could not immediately be confirmed with the giant reflectors of the Mount Wilson Observatory in California. As experts well know, these instruments are not much suited for the photography of formations of low-surface brightness because of their large focal ratios (aperture to focal length about 1 to 5.5). A censoring committee which had been *appointed* (not elected by the faculty) by the authorities of the Carnegie Institution of Washington administrating the Mount Wilson Observatory and the Palomar Observatory of the California Institute of Technology, therefore prevented me from publishing my results in any of the leading official American scientific journals in astronomy and physics. My discoveries of intergalactic clouds, bridges and jets, which I was forced to publish first in the Swiss technical journal *Experientia* (Vol. 6, p. 441, 1950) have in the meantime been confirmed by numerous observers and have proved of prime importance for our understanding of the large-scale distribution of matter in the universe and its evolution (see for instance *Ergebnisse der Exakten Naturwissenschaften* [Multiple Galaxies] Vol. 29, 344–385, 1956, and F. Zwicky, *Morphological Astronomy*, Berlin, Springer Verlag, 1957).

A further fundamental extension of our knowledge of cosmic bodies and events was achieved through the prediction from theory of the existence of very compact stellar systems and the subsequent discovery of hundreds of representatives of this fascinating family of new types of material aggregates containing all types of stars, luminous gas clouds and dust. Again my original major paper announcing significant results on these objects was rejected by the leading *American Astrophysical Journal* without any adequate justification. The article was therefore first printed in France (*Comptes Rendus*, t.257, p. 2240, 1963), in Poland (*Acta Astronomica*, Vol. 14, p. 151, 1964), in Germany (*Die Sterne*, Vol. 40, p. 129, 1964), and in Russia (*Proceedings of the Armenian Academy of Sciences*, Vol. 39, p. 167, 1964).

A striking example of the ridiculous consequences that often result from unsound and unsystematic, that is, amorphological, thinking on the part of theoreticians and practitioners of the various sciences is the following: After the successful launching of Sputnik I by the Russians on October 4, 1957, many Americans became unduly worried, and mathematicians and physicists precipitously started making plans for a complete reorganization of teaching schedules for schools at all levels in order to recover lost ground. The "New Mathematics" wasted no time before starting to confuse and torture unsuspecting children and teenagers unmercifully with abstract concepts of the algebra of sets and with group theory, etc., all subjects about which, in former years, only university students in mathematics and physics had heard anything at all. The youngsters furthermore had to learn to add, subtract, multiply, and divide in various number systems of the base 7 or 12 and so on. The startled parents, few of whom could help their sons and daughters with such problems, were told that no one could really understand the multiplication table in the decimal system unless he was able to operate in all of the other systems using bases different from ten. The ultimate result of course was, as I unfortunately had to observe it with my own small daughters, that in the end they were incapable of calculating anything in any system. The greatest absurdity related to the unrealistic attitudes of the type described is that it did not seem to occur to the wise promoters of the new ways of learning that one should do away first with the abominable and time-wasting systems of measuring lengths, velocities, weights, and so on, which are still in common use in the United States of America, England, and some other countries, and introduce units scaled up or down by powers of ten. Thus, for measuring lengths, millimeters, decimeters, meters, decameters, hectometers, and kilometers should be used universally, or going down the scale, microns (10^{-4} cm), and Angstroms (10^{-8} cm). Instead of promoting the CGS (centimeter, gram, second) system, the learned gentlemen dumbfound the children with beautiful theory fit for a Ph.D. candidate, but continue to let them bungle along with inches (subdivided into $\frac{1}{32}$, $\frac{1}{16}$, $\frac{1}{8}$, $\frac{1}{4}$ and $\frac{1}{2}$), feet ($= 12$ inches), yards ($= 3$ feet) and miles ($= 5280$ feet). What these educators are sorely lacking is unbias, civil courage, and power of decision, all of which are indispensable for a sensible morphological approach, and armed with which they could have achieved the transition of the whole world to the practice of a universal and sensible system of measures and dimensions.

Limited and prejudiced thinking on the part of many scientists is often also responsible for rather tragic consequences in their own personal lives. As my colleague Professor R. P. Feynman stated it in a public address on "The Value of Science" at the 1955 meeting of the National Academy of Sciences, held in Pasadena, November 2 to 4, "I believe that a scientist looking at nonscientific problems is just as dumb as the next guy—and when he talks about a nonscientific matter he sounds as naive as anyone untrained in the matter." I cannot really present any voluminous statistical data on this issue, which it would be of importance to investigate more fully. I am nevertheless inclined to be pessimistic when surveying the experiences I have had in the course of half a century in science, observing thousands of my colleagues, their stability of character, their attitude towards justice and really fair dealing, and, most trivial, even their provisions for the welfare of their families, old age, their frequent lack of concern for their widowed or divorced wives, and the lack of care for many essentially orphaned children, whom they have been known to leave irresponsibly to their own fates.

It is not really surprising that under these circumstances the contributions of numerous scientists to the building of a sound and stabilized world remain meager. One can only hope that every scientist not only adopt a more responsible attitude towards the general affairs of the world, but that he also acquaint himself with the morphological approach in order to make his contributions as effective as possible.

We emphasize again that in contradistinction to the run-of-the-mill professor or engineer, the morphologist in his own profession occupies himself both with the solution of special technical problems and with the unbiased evaluation of all results achieved and their practical applications. But going far beyond that, he strives to incorporate his work organically into the activities of the human society as a whole. In this endeavour he will profit from every occasion to demonstrate to his fellow men the power and usefulness of a balanced outlook and show how the morphological approach can be effective in the solutions of problems not only in the sciences and technology but also in the arts, history, politics, language teaching, ethics, and the practice of religions. Every professional morphologist has discovered again and again that his general approach led him without fail to the clear visualization of new and unexpected problems, his occupation with which resulted in a continuous broadening of his personal store of knowledge and experiences as well as an enrichment of the life of the whole community.

Morphological research in the sense described is the study of the intrinsic character and the evolution of material, phenomenological and spiritual structural interrelationships. The *morphological mode of life* in turn profits from the discoveries and inventions made, and from the knowledge gained from such studies, that enable it to progress steadily towards the great goals man has set himself.

This ultimately brings us to the question of all questions: What should our goals actually be? The answer for each one of us is different and depends upon one's own peculiar potentialities, that is, his innate genius, which he must learn to recognize first before he can make the proper choices about how to live his life most satisfactorily and most effectively. In order to guide men in their search for vocations and avocations, morphological research must review the totality of all possible values for which individuals might strive. Technically speaking, the "morphological box of all values" must be established and all of its contents clearly analyzed and described. Every individual may then choose one or more of these values, which he must try to realize in order to make the optimum use of his capabilities and his knowledge for the enrichment of his own life and the stabilization and evolution of the world.

If I were asked for which particular goals I am personally striving in order to make the optimum use of my potentialities, I should put the recognition of the basic aberrations of the human mind and the problem of their elimination in first place. As I have repeatedly stressed in the course of this book, I consider the overcoming of all human aberrations and the recognition and neutralization of all superstitions, dogmas, and prejudices of all sorts as the indispensable prerequisite if we are ever to master the continually growing multitude of conflicts within the community of men. Intensive occupation with these problems and their morphological analysis and evaluation has already yielded numerous and unexpected new insights, which in part will form the subject matter of a future book by the author, entitled *Everyone a Genius*.

Some Problems That Have Been Solved Through the Application of the Morphological Approach

In conclusion, a few fields will be mentioned that have been subjected to a morphological study. For details of the procedures followed the solutions achieved, however, the reader must be referred to the existing literature, some of which is listed at the end of this book.

PROPULSIVE POWER PLANTS

At the beginning of World War II, as director of research of the Aerojet Engineering Corporation in Pasadena, California, I explored the totality of all possible propulsive power plants activated by the energy released from chemical reactions and moving through various external media, that is, vacuum, air, water, and earth. It was found that the symbolic "morphological box" of these jet engines contains 576 entries representing the basic devices possible, all of them characteristically distinct from one another. Of these, previous to my investigation only three were described in the technical literature and had actually been constructed. These three devices are, first, the ordinary rocket, which was built by the Chinese many centuries ago; second, the combination of a reciprocating engine driving a propeller that generates the forward thrust; and third, the so-called aeroduct (originally designated as the athodyd = aerothermodynamic duct by the British, more commonly known as the ramjet). As a hybrid device, Campini in Italy, just before World War II, built a reciprocating engine—jet propulsive power plant, which, however, was not further developed or used.

Unknown to me and to most of the world was the fact that in England and Germany the aeroturbojet had been developed as it is being used today for the propulsion of military and most of the long distance commercial airplanes. Still less was known about the secret work on the aeroresonator invented and first constructed by P. Schmidt in Munich; this device, which I invented independently during the war and for which I hold the United States patent, gained temporary fame as the propulsive power plant of the V-1 missile (Vergeltungswaffe Nummer 1) and became variously known as the buzzbomb engine or the pulsejet.

The inventors of the different engines mentioned above must certainly be credited with having achieved technically ingenious specific devices. On the other hand, the study of the contents of the morphological box of propulsive power plants led to the visualization, invention, and actual construction of whole classes of devices including the aeropulse, hydropulse, aeroresonator, hydroresonator, hydroturbojet, and many other engines, of which several dozen now have actually been built.

As was said before, the inventor and constructor of any isolated type of device often succeeds in doing brilliant engineering, but in most cases he is quite incapable of inventing and building whole groups of new engines by himself. As to more details about the 576 possible types of chemically activated propulsive power plants, the reader may be interested in studying the numerous comprehensive patents already issued and consulting the respective literature (see for instance F. Zwicky, *Morphology of Propulsive Power*, Monograph No. 1 of the Society for Morphological Research, Pasadena, 1962, available at the bookstore of the California Institute of Technology, Pasadena, California).

We must not fail to emphasize that as a result of the invention of so many new types of jet engines, very important problems immediately arose concerning the nature and availability of the best propellants for each engine. It was also necessary to start with the planning and construction of many necessary auxiliary devices, such as injectors, igniters, propellant pumps, nozzles and so on, which were not immediately available and had to be developed to satisfy all the specific requirements for the optimum performance of the systems in question.

MORPHOLOGICAL ASTRONOMY

During the past few decades the morphological approach has been applied in astronomy for the identification of all possible material cosmic objects and for the survey of the sky for their discovery. Remarkable successes have been achieved in particular with the search for supernovae, novae, faint blue stars, pygmy stars, dwarf, pygmy and gnome galaxies, and perhaps most important the discovery of the extended family of compact galaxies, some of which are radio sources, while others are radio-quiescent to the limits observable with our present day instruments. For more details the following summary of articles and books may be consulted:

F. Zwicky and collaborators, *Catalog of Galaxies and of Clusters of Galaxies*, six volumes, Pasadena, California Institute of Technology, 1961, 1963, 1965, 1966; the two last volumes to appear in 1968.

F. Zwicky, "Multiple Galaxies," in *Ergebnisse der Exakten Naturwissenschaften*, Vol. 29, 344, Springer Verlag, 1956.

F. Zwicky, *Morphological Astronomy*, Berlin, Springer Verlag, 1957.

F. Zwicky, "Supernovae," p. 367–423 in the series *Stellar Structure*, Vol. VIII, University of Chicago Press, 1965.

F. Zwicky, "Durchmusterung der Himmelsobjekte," in: *Bild der Wissenschaft*, 1964, July issue, Stuttgart, Germany, Deutsche Verlagsanstalt.

F. Zwicky, "Compact and Dispersed Cosmic Matter," in Vol. V of *Advances in Astronomy and Astrophysics*, Academic Press, New York, 1968.

Morphological research has also led to the invention and perfection of the powerful method of composite analytical photography that has made possible the remarkable analysis of essential structural features of galaxies and cosmic gas and dust clouds (see F. Zwicky, *Morphological Astronomy*, Berlin, Springer Verlag, 1957).

And finally the morphological approach has been most fruitful in the field of instrumentation, resulting in the introduction of many auxiliary devices, which greatly improve the performance of the Schmidt telescopes. One of the most unusual contributions to this field is the construction of the first mosaic transmission gratings. These promise to become of major importance in astronomy once they are being used in sizes covering the full apertures of wide-angle telescopes (see *Die Sterne*, Issue 3/4, 1967).

MODEST MORPHOLOGY

This type of morphological research, according to Professor John Strong of Johns Hopkins University in Baltimore, Maryland, does not necessarily insist upon deducing *all* the solutions of any given problem or investigating all the aspects of given sets of circumstances. As a typical example Strong treats the problem of constructing a straight line (See *Engineering and Science*, California Institute of Technology, May 1964). A straight line can be produced *ab initio* in an absolute manner by various, most interesting methods, or it can be obtained through a series of approximations starting from an initially curved line. Since the number of the conceivable methods is very large, the analysis and evaluation of all of them would be a rather formidable task. Strong therefore starts from a considerate choice of a few methods whose advantages and disadvantages he evaluates before deciding which one to use in practice. He thus proceeds "modestly morphologically" instead of "uncompromisingly morphologically." By this procedure Strong succeeded in solving an old problem that had troubled the best instrument makers for over sixty years, that is the construction of a perfect ruling engine for the production of diffraction gratings. Such gratings, consisting of a great number of parallel and equidistant straight lines engraved on a polished flat or concave metal or glass plate, play an all important role and are absolutely indispensable for spectral analyses in astronomy, physics, chemistry, and engineering technology.

ADDITIONAL MORPHOLOGICAL INVESTIGATIONS

Among the earliest applications of the morphological methods in Germany the studies by W. Stanner on radioelectronic surveying methods should be mentioned (see W. Stanner, *Leitfaden der Funkwertung*, Garmisch-Partenkirchen, 1952).

The inventors of curly yarns and the famous Hellanca stretch fabrics of the textile firm Heberlein and Company, in Wattwil, Switzerland, have extensively investigated the various physical and chemical methods for processing individual fibers, for instance nylon and silk. In collaboration with the author this group of Swiss engineer scientists also explored the totality of the methods with which curly yarn may be manufactured. The morphological approach to specific but many-sided projects of this kind almost invariably yields technically and commercially important results.

Some Future Problems

The recognition and overcoming of the aberrations of the human mind, in my opinion represent the most important tasks to be dealt with through the morphological approach. At the same time, however, it will of course be important to use the new powerful methods for the analysis and solution of numerous more restricted problems confronting us in the sciences, engineering, medicine, the field of law, education, art, politics, national defense, and human behaviour in general, in order to prevent the disintegration or loss of the substantial gains made in the past. Since the world is still oriented superficially and materialistically, it is also rather important, for the time being, to impress it on its own terms, that is with commonly valued achievements, in order to gain the common man's confidence for more profound endeavours. Every morphologist, whether he acts professionally or plays an enjoyable game, must try to demonstrate that his approach is superior to all others and that he is quite capable of competing with any specialist in his own field. He will nevertheless avoid wasting any of his efforts and always try to achieve results that will help him on the way towards the ultimate goal, elimination of the most disastrous human failings and construction of a sound world. With this in mind he will be particularly interested in questions of medicine, psychology, nutrition, overpopulation, traffic and communications, safety, habitation (ekistics), pollution of air, water and earth, and of course the prevention of war and useless slaughter.

One of the obvious prerequisites for success in building a unified world is ease of communication between man and man and between peoples and peoples The use of a synthetic language has not proved a success and perhaps never will, since it lacks the cultural, historic, and sentimental background of the natural languages. I have therefore investigated the problem of the feasibility of multilanguage teaching, the introduction of which would lead to a rapid increase in the number of multilingual individuals. This, I believe, would greatly contribute towards dispelling the distrusts now poisoning relations among the peoples of the world. First tests in this direction have been very encouraging, and a book on multilanguage teaching is therefore in preparation. A first preliminary contribution on this subject will be included in the monograph on methodology mentioned in the appended bibliography.

Conclusions and Recommendations

Morphological thought and action not only enable us to reach various types of goals in the most effective manner, they transform many otherwise tiresome chores into pleasurable ones. The morphologist must of course not allow his imagination under all circumstances to freely roam the vast vistas open to him especially not when driving his car. One of his most fundamental principles in fact is that no one should do two things at the same time, unless he is born to it or has had special training to avoid accidents caused by divided attention. Unfortunately we shall not be in a position for some time to come to enjoy all of the pleasurable and humorous aspects of the morphological mode of life fully, since we must first deal with the threatening interferences caused by the numerous rampant aberrations of the human mind. This holding action is necessary in order to preserve at least the status quo and not allow destructive actions to precipitate the world into a chaos of spiritual and material disorder.

Although problems of the most difficult kind still confront us, no determined morphologist will give up hope that eventually we shall achieve the impossible through the morphological approach. And in the meantime, during some leisure hours of solitary contemplation we shall allow ourselves the luxury of dreaming about a clean world, which does not disgust us, and in which every individual has realized his genius and is happily prepared to recognize the fact that in some way or another everyone of his fellow men is unique, incomparable, and irreplaceable. For the morphologists a clean world, realization of one's genius and recognition of the worth of each and every individual are the three necessary and sufficient conditions for the achievement of that ultimate state of satisfaction and happiness that men for thousands of years have sought in vain to reach.

Additional Writings of the Author on Morphological Research

1. *Report on Certain Phases of War Research in Germany*, published by Headquarters Air Materiel Command, Wright Field, Ohio, January, 1947 (book, 188 pp.).
2. "Morphologische Forschung," in *Helvetica Physica Acta*, 23 (1950), 223.
3. "Multiple Galaxies," in: *Ergebnisse der exakten Naturwissenschaften*, Vol. 29, 344–85. Berlin, Springer Verlag, 1956.
4. "The Morphological Method and Vector Associations, in La Méthode dans les Sciences Modernes," *Editions Science et Industrie*, Paris, 1958.
5. *Morphologische Forschung*, Kommissionsverlag, Buchdruckerei Winterthur AG, 1958 (book, 111 pp., out of print).
6. *Morphological Astronomy*, Berlin, Springer Verlag, 1957 (book, 299 pp.).
7. F. Zwicky and collaborators: *Catalogue of Galaxies and Clusters of Galaxies*, Vol. I (1961), II (1963), V (1965), III (1966), Pasadena, California Institute of Technology, (Vol. IV and VI in press).
8. *Morphology of Propulsive Power*. Monograph No. 1 of the Society for Morphological Research, Pasadena, 1962 (book, 382 pp.).
9. "Supernovae," in: *Stars and Stellar Systems*, Vol. VIII, *Stellar Structure*, Chicago, The University of Chicago Press, 1965.
10. "Durchmusterung der Himmelsobjekte," in: *Bild der Wissenschaft*, 1 (1964), Part 5, 31–41, Stuttgart, Germany.
11. "Compact and Dispersed Cosmic Matter," in *Advances in Astronomy and Astrophysics*, Vol. V, New York, Academic Press, Inc., 1968.
12. *New Methods of Thought and Procedure*, edited by F. Zwicky and A. G. Wilson, New York, Springer Verlag, 1967.

Inventions Made and Patents Obtained by the Author With the Aid of the Morphological Approach

			Inventor
US	2 426 526	Two piece jet thrust motor	Zwicky and Rutishauser, et al.
US	2 433 943	Operation of jet propulsion motors with Nitroparaffin	Zwicky, et al.
Brit.	602 807	Improvements in jet propulsion apparatus	Zwicky
US	2 811 431	Operation of thrust motors with high impulse, and fuel for same	Zwicky, et al.
US	2 815 271	Fuel containing Nitromethane and Nitroethane	Zwicky
US	2 821 838	Jet propulsion device for operation through fluid medium and method of operating it	Zwicky
US	2 914 913	Apparatus and method for jet propulsion through water by use of water reactive propellant	Zwicky
US	2 932 943	Jet propulsion device for operation through a fluid medium	Zwicky
US	2 974 626	Apparatus for jet propulsion through water	Zwicky
US	3 044 252	Inverted Hydropulse	Zwicky
US	3 044 253	Method and apparatus for jet propulsion through water	Zwicky
US	3 048 007	Decomposition of Nitroparaffin in jet propulsion motor operation	Zwicky
US	3 121 992	Decomposition of Nitroparaffins in jet propulsion motor operation	Zwicky, et al.
US	3 135 205	Coruscative ballistic device	Zwicky
US	3 137 994	Device and method for jet propulsion through a water medium	Zwicky
US	3 253 511	Launching process and apparatus	Zwicky

Index

266 INDEX